The Observer's Books

THE OBSERVER'S BOOK OF

SEA FISHES

By
A. LAURENCE WELLS

Describing
ONE HUNDRED AND
SIXTY-FOUR SPECIES
with 125 illustrations
62 of which are in full colour

FREDERICK WARNE & CO. LTD.
FREDERICK WARNE & CO. INC.
LONDON · NEW YORK

Printed in Great Britain

PREFACE

THIS book is intended to provide a means of recognizing all the different species of fish likely to be found in the seas around us or in the shallows and rock pools of our coasts, attached to the hook at the end of a fishing line, or at the fishmonger's.

Those who are fortunate enough to be able to accompany an inshore trawlerman in the course of his labours should also find this book of use in identifying the 'rubbish' which is thrown overboard. In this material there are often many species of fishes of little or no use to the fisherman but which are of great interest to the man in the street.

Some fishes are dealt with more fully than others, even though they may not be of any great economic importance or of general occurrence. This is because their life stories may be of particular interest or because they have been the object of detailed study. Only the very rare species have been omitted.

If the text interests and if, with the plates, it helps in the identification of such marine fishes as come the reader's way then the author will feel that he has achieved his purpose.

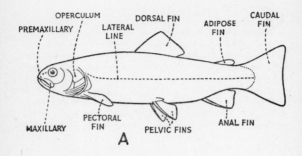

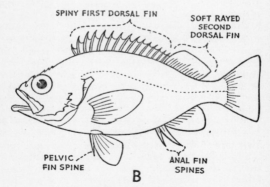

External features of a fish

INTRODUCTION

A GLANCE at a map of the world, no matter of which particular projection, will show the peculiar position of the British Isles in respect of the adjacent seas, each of which has its own specialized type of population both as regards fishes and other marine organisms.

The result is a wide range of fish groups, each with its peculiar idiosyncrasies in the matter of temperature, salinity, depths and type of food.

Thus, from the north, the Arctic Seas rich in planktonic and other crustacea, abound in the various members of the cod tribe. The seas off Norway and the Baltic Sea itself are ideally suited for the needs of the herring and the sprat, especially in their young state. Incidentally, the herring of less than a year old is known as 'sild' and is so called when canned in olive oil; the sprat of any age, when canned, is known as 'brisling'; the 'sardine' of commerce is the young of the pilchard.

The last named is one of the many species of Mediterranean and Bay of Biscay fishes which visit our south-west peninsula in great numbers. The pilchard has even been known to come into the North Sea in large numbers on rare occasions. Other Mediterranean fishes, as well as those from the warm parts of the Atlantic, of strong swimming habits, venture into our waters in search of food.

Then there are the fishes of the Gulf Stream.

that river of warm water flowing from the Gulf of Florida and known also as the Florida Current or the Atlantic Drift, which impinges on the more westerly parts of our islands. For the most part these are strangers of unfamiliar shapes and colours which seem to be sent to puzzle the longshoremen of the Irish sea coasts and those of the west coasts of Ireland and Scotland and of Devon and Cornwall. Sometimes a straggler will enter the North Sea and, if captured, will cause considerable excitement. These rare fishes are not dealt with in this book; Dr. Jenkins's book* does them full justice, as it also does to those rare visitors from the great depths, some of which are only known from single specimens found in the stomachs of other rare fishes from beyond the continental shelf off the south-west coast of Ireland.

At this point it is only right to dilate somewhat on this aspect of continental geography, so often referred to and yet so rarely explained. Around all continental land masses the shores shelve seawards towards the ocean depths. The extent of this shelf varies considerably, but it can be assessed as being from five to two hundred miles or even more from the extreme shores of such land masses. This is the home of many of the larger fishes on which we depend for our food, the cod, haddock, halibut and so forth. There they find an abundance of their favourite foods.

Invariably, from the edge of this shelf, the water becomes rapidly deeper and, not infrequently, the sea floor falls away to the abyssal depths which, for all our modern methods of research, are still an almost unknown world.

* THE FISHES OF THE BRITISH ISLES, by J. Travis Jenkins, D.Sc., Ph.D., *Warne*.

In British waters there are two specialized types of fish which, in their season, are always with us. Of those which come from a period of gorging on sea foods to spawn either in the estuaries or in the sweet waters at the head of the rivers, the salmon is a classic example, as is also the sea trout. The lamprey, the lump fish on occasion, the smelt and other species seem to prefer the brackish part of the estuaries. Strangely enough, although in the region of the Caspian and other sturgeon seas, that fish enters the rivers to spawn, it does not seem to do so in the British estuaries where it is so frequently found.

The other type of fish in this category is the common eel which grows to maturity in the freshwater ponds, lakes, rivers and streams and, at the appropriate time, journeys to the estuaries where it will remain for several months, getting used to the extra salinity of the water, before setting out for the spawning grounds in the great depths of the tropical Atlantic waters, somewhere between the Azores and the Bahamas. The conger eel, although it has similar breeding habits, is essentially a creature of the sea, but in the matter of its breeding grounds I would not like to commit myself, other than that they must be considerably nearer our shores than those of its silvery relative.

Then, last but by no means least, there are our native fishes which, for the most part, are small in size: the sand eels, the gobies, the dab, flounder and other flat fishes of their kind, the whiting and the rocklings, the wrasses and the gurnards and many others. All are lovers of the coast, rocky, sandy or muddy, according to their inclination.

Now, we must consider the fishes themselves, the

groups into which they fall and their own exterior characteristics.

Firstly, they fall into three distinct classes. The first of these, starting from the lowest rung of the ladder, that being the order in which they are dealt with in this book, is the class Marsipobranchii, so called from the pouch-like form the gill chambers take. In this class we have only the lampreys and the hag-fish, all of which are eel-like in shape and more or less externally parasitic on other fishes. The basking shark seems to be one of their favourite victims.

Next there is the class Selachii, the sharks and rays which differ in several particulars from the true fishes which comprise the class Pisces, the bony fishes. Here we encounter a peculiarity of the finny tribe: it is impossible to generalize about them for there are so many exceptions. Still, we are able to separate the Selachii from the 'true' or bony fishes by applying several rule-of-thumb methods on the principle that if one fails then another will succeed.

In the first place, the bones in the Selachii are of a gristly or cartilaginous nature and only harden with old age. The skin does not possess scales but has bony spines or plates composed mostly of lime—in the thornback ray these plates bear hard and sharp curved spines, while in some sharks the spines are small and closely set and give the skin the feel and quality of sandpaper. The gills, too, are different. They are slits, five on each side of the head except in the order Hexanchidae in which there are six gill slits on each side. The gill slits do not possess covers.

The mouth, without exception, is on the under-side of the head with the snout projecting some distance beyond it according to the species and in nearly all species ending in a point. The tail, too, is different, the upper lobe being considerably longer than the lower one; this is because the spinal column continues along the upper lobe. Although they cannot weep, not having any lachrymal glands, some of the sharks have a form of eyelid.

The members of this class fall into five orders (six if the recently discovered fossil form Cratoselache is included), three of which are only known as fossils. This leaves the order Pleurotremata in which are the sharks and dogfishes and the order Hypotremata in which are the skates and rays. Here it might be well to point out that the skates can be likened to dogfishes which have been put through the mangle for in most respects they are much alike. Midway between the sharks and the rays (but in the same order as the former) is the monkfish which is not quite so flat as a skate nor yet so round as a shark.

A sub-class Holocephali is represented by the chimaera or rabbit fish, a deep-water fish which on rare occasions is taken by our deep-sea trawlers.

The majority of 'fishes' of the present day and of our own shores come within the class Pisces, a class which the great naturalist of the eighteenth century, John Ray, defined as being 'animals with blood, breathing by gills, provided with a single ventricle of the heart, covered with scales or naked,' a most apt and all-embracing definition. Later he recanted somewhat for he realized that this definition excluded the whales, which, of course, it should do and so he invented a definition which included the two.

The class Pisces is divided into three sub-classes,

the Palaeopterygii, the Crossopterygii and the Neopterygii. So far as we are concerned in this country the first named is represented by only one order, the Chondrostei, and that by only one species, the sturgeon, which is only an occasional visitor in any case. The second class is not represented at all save in a fossil state. The last named includes practically all of the bony fishes and is divided into about thirty-one orders of which about nineteen are commonly represented in the seas around Britain.

The first of these orders is the Isospondyli, a most important order indeed for it includes all of the salmon kind as well as the herring, sprat, pilchard and their relations. The members of this order all possess an air bladder which is connected with the gullet by a duct. Moreover, the pelvic fins are situated at about the middle of the abdominal region.

The next order of interest to us is the order Apodes, the eels, distinguished by their familiar elongated bodies of cylindrical form, by the absence of pelvic fins and by the continuing of the ventral and dorsal fins into the tail. In most species of eel the scales are entirely absent but in some species, such as the common eel, they are very small indeed and are buried in the skin. This eel and the conger are the only common British eels, but from time to time at rare intervals gales from the west and south-west bring strange eels from the depths of the western ocean.

There is another order of fishes, the Synentognathi, which are of eel-like form, and this order includes the saury pike, the garfish and the flying fish. In this order there is one dorsal fin placed well towards the tail end of the fish and consisting of a small number of rays. The mouth is formed of two elongated beaks with the lower one the longer. In this order the air bladder has no opening. Ordinarily, the pectoral fin is small, but in the flying fish it is greatly enlarged and the mouth is not elongated. The flying fish is a very rare visitor to our shores yet there is an authentic record of one having been captured in the Medway as far up river as Rochester. This was towards the end of September 1898, and the fish was seen by a man who struck at it with his walking stick (it was probably 'flying' at the time) and so captured it. Dr. James Murie preserved it in spirit, but when he died at the age of 93 in the early 'twenties it was destroyed with the rest of his collection.

Next come the Pipe Fishes of the order Solenichthyes, all of which are feeble swimmers. They have the snout prolonged into a tube with a tiny mouth and the fins are small and not very effective for swimming purposes. More often than not they swim in an upright position and this is especially so with the Sea Horse, the most curious member of this most curious group. None are of any economic value whatever.

Far more important to mankind are many species of the next order, the Anacanthini. They are distinguished by the fact that the fin-rays are all soft and flexible and by the absence of any spines on the head, or any other part of the body, for that matter. The scales, however, are generally large and stout and furnished with a spiny border. In this order is the cod and the other valuable food fishes of its kind : the hake, haddock, whiting, ling, etc. Generally speaking, the members of this family are distinguished by three separate dorsal fins and a barbel or barbels depending from the lower jaw, but there are exceptions. With the flatfishes they form by far the most valuable food fishes the seas have to offer, yet again, as with the flatfishes, some species are of very little use to man save as food for the larger and more valuable kinds. But here I would like to emphasize that the object of this book is not to dilate on the value of fishes to man. Of far greater interest, in my opinion, is the value of the fishes to themselves, the manner in which each particular species solves the many problems that life sets them.

In the order Allotriognathi only one species pays us more than just the odd visit. It is the opah, up to four feet in length and about the most beautiful of the fishes of the Atlantic.

The John Dory, a fairly common fish of the south-west coast and the less common boar fish belong to the order Zeomorphi, fishes with deep, thin bodies and long fins. They are designed for hovering rather than for swimming.

The next order, the Percomorphi, contains more species of British sea fishes than does any other : the bass, horse mackerel, red mullet, the various sea breams, the wrasses, the sand eels, the weevers, mackerel, tunny and the numerous gobies, blennies, the catfish, the sand smelt and the grey mullet, to name but a few. There are two dorsal fins, the rays of some of which, as well as those of the pelvic and ventral fins, are stiff and spiny. Some are of minute size, such as certain of the gobies whilst others are huge, the tunny for example. The perch of the lakes and rivers is typical of this order.

The members of the order Scleroparei are even

more heavily armoured than are those of the foregoing; for example, the gurnards, sea scorpions and sticklebacks.

The sole, halibut, turbot, brill, plaice and dab, as well as many other species of lesser culinary repute, are included in the order Heterosomata. These are the flatfishes, normally creatures of the sea bed but also well capable of rising to the upper layers of the water in search of food. They swim on their sides—not on their stomachs as do the skates and rays—and their curious early development is dealt with later on in this book. The dorsal and ventral fins extend from the head nearly to the tail, in some species even from in front of the eyes right to the tail itself. At one time they were included in the same order as the cod kind, largely because in both the air bladder is closed and the rays of the fins are flexible and jointed or soft. In other words, they are spineless. Only the flatfishes of the temperate waters, whether north or south of the equator, are of much commercial value. There are a few exceptions only.

The strange looking snail-like fishes, the suckers, are in the order Xenopterygii. They are remarkable for the sucker on their underside which is formed partly from the pelvic fin and a projection from the coracoid bone of the shoulder girdle.

Finally, in this short review of the various orders and principal representatives, there is the order Pediculati—the angler fishes. Although several species from the depths of the Atlantic have been recorded in rare instances, only one species can, by any stretch of the imagination, be regarded as being British. This is the common angler fish, the well-known fishing frog.

From the foregoing brief review of the various orders of fishes it will be noticed that the systematists base their major divisions on whether there is an air bladder or not and, if there is one, on whether it is closed or not. Another consideration is whether the fins, are soft, jointed or otherwise flexible or whether some are hard and spiny. Another is the position of the pelvic fins. Thus the broad distinctions are fairly obvious and follow a reasonably well-defined pattern. It is when we come to the finer divisions that the yardstick seems to vary from one generation to another and so it is quite possible that maybe only a few years hence the whole order of classification will be rearranged.

Nevertheless, in great measure, the system suggested by Peter Artedi, the Swedish naturalist who has justifiably been called the Father of Ichthyology, is still a basic consideration. In 1734, at the early age of 29, he was accidentally drowned in one of Amsterdam's canals. Fortunately for posterity his manuscripts were rescued by an English gentleman by the name of Cliffort and by him handed to the great Linnaeus, a one-time fellow student of Artedi at Upsala University. Linnaeus slightly amended the system and embodied it in his *Systema Naturae*, the principal difference being that he gave binominal terms to the fishes described (and classified) by his friend.

In the matter of the early study of living creatures it is quite possible that the study of fishes slightly preceded that of the other organisms. In any case, Aristotle, surely one of the greatest of all naturalists, as far back as about 340 B.C., had a very sound knowledge of the anatomy, mode of reproduction and migrations of fishes. Allowing for the odd exceptions, his description of the general structure of fishes is surprisingly comprehensive and accurate. I quote from part of it:

'The special characteristics of the true fishes consist in the branchiae and fins, the majority having four fins, but the elongated ones, such as the eels, having two only. Some, such as the Muraena, lack the fins altogether. The Rays swim with the whole of their body, which is spread out. The branchiae are sometimes furnished with an opercle or gill-covering, sometimes without one, as is the case in the cartilaginous fishes [i.e. the skates and rays].'

He continues: 'No fish has hairs or feathers; most are covered with scales, but some have a rough or smooth skin. The tongue is hard, often bearing teeth; and sometimes so much adherent that it seems to be wanting. The eyes have no lids; nor are any ears or nostrils visible, for what takes the place of nostrils is a blind cavity. Nevertheless, they have the senses of tasting, smelling and hearing. All have blood. All scaly fishes are oviparous, but the cartilaginous fishes are viviparous. All have a heart, liver and gall-bladder; but kidneys and urinary bladder are absent. They vary much in the structure of their intestines; for whilst the mullet has a fleshy stomach, like a bird, others have no stomachic dilatation. Pyloric coeca are close to the stomach and are variable in number; there are even some, like the majority of cartilaginous fishes, which have none whatever. Two bodies are situated along the spine, which have the function of testicles, and open towards the vent, which are much enlarged in the spawning season. The scales harden with age. Not being provided with lungs, they have no voice, but several can emit grunting sounds. They sleep like other animals.'

This, I think, covers the ground very nicely. For about eighteen hundred years the rest of mankind seemed to think so too and no one appears to have added one iota to the literature on fishes—with the possible exception of Ausonius, a Roman poet and physician of the fourth century, A.D. He wrote a poem about the River Moselle which he described in great detail, especially the fishes. Otherwise, there was a void until John Ray of Essex started a new wave of learning in the seventeenth century. From then onwards the study of fishes widened and deepened in its scope, even to the discovery of living specimens of two types of fishes which were thought to have been extinct for millions of years. These were the Ceratodus, a freshwater fish from Northern Australia which seems to live on fallen leaves from trees and which was discovered in 1871, and the Coelacanth found in 1938 nine miles off East London, South Africa.

Only the most hidebound of people would deny that there are yet many more such exciting fishes still surviving in the unfished parts of the world's seas—possibly even the fabulous sea serpent.

We must now move from the obvious features of the fish as outlined by Aristotle so many centuries ago, to the less readily observed and understood aspects of the finny creatures of the waters, that is to say, those aspects controlled by the nervous system which, in man, are erroneously referred to as 'the five senses.' In fishes, so far as can be ascertained, there are six senses: the five with which we are popularly accredited—sight, hearing, touch, smell and taste—and an additional sense controlled by a line of nerves running along each side of the body from head to tail. In some species this lateral line is well defined, in the dab, for example, and the horse mackerel. If the lateral line in such fishes is examined it will be found to consist of tough bundles of nerves situated immediately behind specialized scales, scales with an aperture in their centre. Thus the nerves are more or less exposed to the water, and anyone who has had an exposed nerve in a tooth will know just how sensitive such a nerve can be. I am not, of course, suggesting that the fishy nerve is anything like so sensitive as ours are. I sincerely hope not, otherwise I have been guilty of inflicting considerable pain on a number of fishes in my time.

In considering the nervous system of fishes it must be borne in mind that it has to operate in a somewhat different medium from that in which ours operates. Thus, the nerves of the lateral line must, logically speaking, be highly sensitive to the slightest movement in the water, whether set up by a sound wave or by some organism or body moving in the near vicinity. By this means, it is assumed, sprats, herrings, mackerel and other fishes which move about in shoals are able to sense the direction the leader decides to take. The sound waves picked up by the lateral line are of very low frequency, at the same end of the scale as the very lowest notes the human ear is capable of receiving.

That the fish can hear, although it does not possess the elaborate apparatus of the higher animals, has been proved conclusively. I do not refer to the reaction following the tapping of the glass side of an aquarium. To the fish this is comparable to the vibrations our fingers feel when a glass or bell has been struck. I mean actual hearing by means of a special auditory organ—in short, by means of an ear. It has been further proved that in fishes in which the air bladder is connected with the ear hearing is much more acute. The minnow and the eel are in this category.

In higher animals, in human beings at any rate, the sense of hearing is closely allied with the gift of speech. Until quite recently the fish was considered as being without that gift and the bottom of the sea was thought to be as silent as the grave. During the recent war it was shown that, instead of being the dumb creature it has always been believed to be, a fish is a most voluble and noisy chatterbox. The United States navy developed an extremely sensitive underwater microphone for the purpose of detecting submarines. When they tried it out the whole thing was a fiasco, for all that could be heard was the booming, grunting, screeching, gurgling and wheezing of, not only fishes, but other marine organisms as well. Until a method of screening the instrument from those noises was evolved they were unable to use it.

In the matter of sight in fishes there is considerable dissention, especially among anglers. The oculist seems to be in no doubt about the matter and he will, if you ask him about it, tie you up in all kinds of knots with this theory and with that, refraction and light rays and the different shape of the lens of the fish's eye and a lot of other things bewildering to the layman. At the slightest provocation he will draw diagrams and angles and propound theory after theory and when two of them get together then indeed the mathematics get higher and higher. The student of fish, however, is far less interested in what might be the case, no matter how well supported by logic, than in what experiment proves, and very few experiments have been carried out on underwater vision in fishes. That they can see what is happening out of the water, however, we have ample proof. Four different species of fishes quite voluntarily provide this proof. One species is the common trout, which will snap at a fly before it lands on the water. This is noticeable not only when trout are rising to the angler's lure but also when the mayfly emerge to give them their annual mayfly banquet.

Then there is the archer fish (Toxotes) from the streams of Siam which also lives on insects. By squirting a jet of water at insects on the overhanging plant stems and twigs and so knocking them senseless into the water, this fish earns its dinner. Its aim and sense of direction is uncanny, insects on twigs as far above the water as three feet are hit with ease, positive proof that the fish can see very clearly into the air.

The golden orfe, a popular fish with pond keepers in this country, is very partial to gnats and other insects which hover over the water. In the early evening when such insects seem to assemble it is by no means unusual to see the orfe leap out of the water and fall back with a splash, and an insect.

The curious South American anableps has four eyes, or, more correctly its two eyes are divided horizontally. Thus, it can swim on the surface and see what is happening in the great world outside with its top pair and, at the same time, keep its eyes on the alert under the water. Fishes do not have eyelids nor yet lachrymal glands—living as they do in a liquid element their eyes are continually being bathed. But the anableps has to dip its head into the water every few minutes to prevent the upper part of its eyes from drying in the air.

Another point of interest about the sight of fishes is their quite definite ability to distinguish one bright colour from another. This is obvious in two species of tropical fishes, the jewel fish or red cichlid, *Hemichromis bimaculatus*, from Africa and the Jack Dempsey, *Cichlasoma biocellatum*, from Brazil. In both species the parents have the unusual quality in fishes of looking after their respective offspring even after they have left the egg. When the parents scent danger they sharply jerk their fins and the babies come hurrying to their side. If the parents are removed, in the case of the former species, and a red disc is suspended in the water and wriggled about, the infants will rush to the disc. The adults of the latter species are blue in colour and their young will react in the same manner to a blue disc. If, in an aquarium, a mixture of the infants of the two species are housed without any of the parents, the young of the red cichlid will assemble at a red disc wriggled about at one end of the aquarium whilst the young of the Jack Dempsey will congregate around a blue disc similarly wriggled about, not just the once, but always.

I mention this ability of fishes to distinguish colours for the benefit of anglers who may feel inclined to try out baits of different colours. Not, of course, that the sea is the best of places in which to distinguish one colour from another.

The reason why I am occupying so much of this

foreword with accounts of the fish's sensory system and reactions to exterior influences is that these are points often enquired about by anglers and observers generally. To continue with the next of its senses to be discussed, that of feeling as distinct from the feeling of pain, in this respect the lateral line has already been mentioned. But there are other specialized concentrations of nerves and mostly these are found either in fishes with poor vision or in those which live on the muddy sea bed. These generally possess barbels with which they feel their way about and also locate the molluscs and worms on which they usually feed.

That these barbels are highly sensitive I have had ample proof. For about six years I have kept a freshwater catfish in an aquarium and as it is about nine inches in length and has a monstrous mouth and appetite it lives alone. No fish can live with it for when they are not looking it bites big lumps out of them and by this means it killed two quite large goldfish. Its favourite meal is a live newt which it swallows at one gulp. So it spends its days in quiet contemplation, sometimes not moving at all for hours on end. The eyes are very small and of little service and they cannot see even a pencil when it is brought right up close. But if one of its fringe of 'feelers' is touched ever so lightly it shoots off at once.

From this same fish I learned several things about the ways of fishes that I did not know of before or which I had never seen demonstrated. Firstly, when a piece of meat is dropped into the water there is no reaction on the part of the fish for about ten seconds, then all at once it rouses itself and proceeds to career round and round the bottom of the tank. As soon as one of the feelers touches the meat, the fish immediately engulfs it with the rapidity of a striking snake. This lightning-like reaction is an essential for a fish with such poor sight in dealing with the speedy creatures on which it feeds. A stickleback has just to flick against one of those hypersensitive feelers to seal its doom.

Another equally spectacular feature of this particular fish is its method of separating the fat from the lean part of the butcher's meat on which it is sometimes fed. Ordinarily, it will reject fat and so I gave it some minced meat to see what would happen. It gulped the meat down in great lumps but some time later I found lumps of fat floating about in the water. On watching it closely the next time I fed it I discovered how it managed this separating act. The lean meat disappeared down its throat and the fat pieces were discharged through its gill openings. I have since wondered if, in the wild state, a fish ever has to deal in a similar manner with the food it gleans.

The barbels or feelers of many fishes, particularly the freshwater and marine catfish, are well equipped with taste buds as well as sensitive nerves. Some, especially those living in the dark, have taste buds all over their bodies including their tails.

Like the sharks, the catfish have an acute sense of smell but I do not think their sense of smell is anything like so acute as that of the sharks, or of the pirana of South America. But my catfish has shown me that if, for some strange reason, it has not noticed the smell of blood from the proffered meat within a minute or so, then it never will. As soon as the blood has been washed out by the water, then the meat no longer attracts it. In fishes with keen sight, of course, as soon as they see the meat they go for it whether it is washed out or not.

Earlier in this introduction I referred to the reaction of fishes to pain. Now, this is an aspect of the fish which is often a topic for discussion but it is generally approached from the wrong angle. 'Do fishes feel pain?' is usually the question, and the answer is 'Of course they feel pain.' Why else should their nervous system be such as it is? But if the question is 'Do fishes feel pain in the same degree that we do?' then the answer must be 'No,' for their nervous system is not so highly developed as ours. Moreover, their brain lacks the cerebral cortex, that part of our brain in which we store up our conscious association of ideas, and so the mental impression of pain has no houseroom and the pain is soon forgotten. At least, I hope so.

CLASSIFIED INDEX

TO ORDERS, FAMILIES, GENERA, AND SPECIES DESCRIBED IN THIS WORK

Class MARSIPOBRANCHII
Order HYPEROARTIA

PETROMYZONIDAE

Sea Lamprey. *Petromyzon marinus*, Linn.

Lampern. *Lampetra fluviatilis* (Linn.)=*Petromyzon fluviatilis*, Day.

Brook Lamprey. *Lampetra planeri* (Bloch)=*Petromyzon branchialis*, Day.

Class SELACHII
Sub-Class EUSELACHII
Order PLEUROTREMATA

LAMNIDAE

Porbeagle. *Lamna cornubica* (Gmelin).

Basking Shark. *Cetorhinus maximus* (Gunner)= *Selache maxima*, Day.

Thresher. *Alopias vulpes* (Gmelin).

SCYLIORHINIDAE

Greater-spotted Dogfish. *Scyliorhinus stellaris* (Linn.) =*Scyllium catulus*, Day.

Lesser-spotted Dogfish. *Scyliorhinus caniculus* (Linn.).

CARCHARINIDAE

Blue Shark. *Carcharinus glaucus* (Linn.)=*Carcharias glaucus*, Day.

Tope. *Eugaleus galeus* (Linn.)=*Galeus vulgaris*, Day.

Smooth Hound. *Mustelus mustelus* (Linn.)=*M. vulgaris*, Day.

Hammerhead Shark. *Sphyrna zygaena* (Linn.)= *Zygaena malleus*, Day.

SQUALIDAE

Piked Dogfish. *Squalus acanthias*, Linn.=*Acanthias vulgaris*, Day.

Greenland Shark. *Somniosus microcephalus* (Schneider) =*Laemargus microcephalus*, Day.

SQUATINIDAE

Monk-fish. *Squatina squatina* (Linn.)=*Rhina squatina*, Day.

Order HYPOTREMATA
RAJIDAE

Spotted Ray. *Raja montagui*, Fowler=*R. maculata*, Day.

Thornback Ray. *Raja clavata*, Linn.

Cuckoo Ray. *Raja naevus*, Müller and Henle=*R. circularis*, Day.

Sandy Ray. *Raja circularis*, Couch.

White Skate. *Raja marginata*, Lacepède=*R. alba*, Day.

Common Skate. *Raja batis*, Linn.

Flapper Skate. *Raja macrorhynchus*, Rafinesque.

TRYGONIDAE

Sting Ray. *Trygon pastinaca*
(Linn.).

MYLIOBATIDAE

Eagle Ray. *Myliobatis aquila*
(Linn.).

Class PISCES
Sub-Class PALAEOPTERYGII
Order CHONDROSTEI

ACIPENSERIDAE

Sturgeon. *Acipenser sturio*, Linn.

Sub-Class NEOPTERYGII
Order ISOSPONDYLI

CLUPEIDAE

Herring. *Clupea harengus*, Linn.
Sprat. *Clupea sprattus*, Linn.
Allis Shad. *Alosa alosa* (Linn.)=*Clupea alosa*, Day.
Twaite Shad. *Alosa finta* (Cuvier)=*Clupea finta*, Day.
Pilchard. *Sardina pilchardus* (Walbaum)=*Clupea
pilchardus*, Day.
Anchovy. *Engraulis encrasicholus* (Linn.).

SALMONIDAE

Salmon. *Salmo salar*, Linn.
Trout. *Salmo trutta*, Linn.

OSMERIDAE

Smelt. *Osmerus eperlanus* (Linn.).

Order APODES

ANGUILLIDAE

Eel. *Anguilla anguilla* (Linn.) = *A. vulgaris*, Day.

CONGRIDAE

Conger. *Conger conger* (Linn.) = *C. vulgaris*, Day.

Order SYNENTOGNATHI

SCOMBERESOCIDAE

Skipper or Saury. *Scomberesox saurus* (Walbaum).

BELONIDAE

Garfish. *Belone belone* (Linn.) = *B. vulgaris*, Day.

Order SOLENICHTHYES

SYNGNATHIDAE

Snake Pipe-fish. *Entelurus aequoreus* (Linn.) = *Nerophis aequoreus*, Day.
Straight-nosed Pipe-fish. *Nerophis ophidion* (Linn.).
Worm Pipe-fish. *Nerophis lumbriciformis* (Yarrell).
Great Pipe-fish, *Syngnathus acus*, Linn.

Syngnathus rostellatus, Nilsson.
Broad-nosed Pipe-fish. *Siphonostoma typhle* (Linn.).

Sea Horse. *Hippocampus hippocampus* (Linn.)=*H. antiquorum*, Day.

Order ANACANTHINI

MERLUCCIIDAE

Hake. *Merluccius merluccius* (Linn.)=*M. vulgaris*, Day.

GADIDAE

Cod. *Gadus callarias* (Linn.)=*G. morrhua*, Day.

Haddock. *Gadus aeglifinus*, Linn.
Bib. *Gadus luscus*, Linn.
Poor Cod. *Gadus minutus*, Linn.
Whiting. *Gadus merlangus*, Linn.
Coal-fish. *Gadus virens*, Linn.
Pollack. *Gadus pollachius*, Linn.
Greater Fork-beard. *Urophycis blennoides* (Brünnich) =*Phycis blennoides*, Day.
Ling. *Molva molva* (Linn.)=*M. vulgaris*, Day
Five-bearded Rockling. *Onos mustelus* (Linn.)= *Motella mustela*, Day.
Four-bearded Rockling. *Onos cimbrius* (Linn.)= *Motella cimbria*, Day.
Three-bearded Rockling. *Onos tricirratus* (Bloch)= *Motella tricirrata*, Day.
Lesser Fork-beard. *Raniceps raninus* (Linn.).
Torsk. *Brosme brosme* (Müller)=*Brosmius brosme*, Day.

Order ALLOTRIOGNATHI

LAMPRIDIDAE

Opah *Lampris luna* (Gmelin).

Order ZEOMORPHI

ZEIDAE

John Dory. *Zeus faber*, Linn.

CAPROIDAE

Boar-fish. *Capros aper* (Linn.).

Order PERCOMORPHI

SERRANIDAE

Bass. *Morone labrax* (Linn.).
= *Labrax lupus*, Day.

Stone Basse. *Polyprion americanus* (Schneider)= *P. cernium*, Day.
Dusky Perch. *Epinephelus gigas* (Brünnich)= *Serranus gigas*, Day.
Comber. *Serranus cabrilla* (Linn.).

CARANGIDAE

Horse Mackerel. *Trachurus trachurus* (Linn.)= *Caranx trachurus*, Day.

Pilot-fish. *Naucrates ductor* (Linn.).
Glaucus. *Trachinotus glaucus* (Linn.)= *Lichia glauca*, Day.

BRAMIDAE

Ray's Bream. *Brama raii* (Bloch).

Brama longipinnis, Lowe.

SCIAENIDAE

Meagre.   *Sciaena aquila*, Risso.

MULLIDAE

Red Mullet.   *Mullus surmuletus*,
   Linn. = *M. barbatus*, Day.

SPARIDAE

Dentex.   *Dentex dentex* (Gmelin) = *D. vulgaris*, Day.

Common Sea Bream.   *Pagellus
   centrodontus* (De la Roche).

Spanish Bream.   *Pagellus bogaraveo* (Brünnich).
Axillary Bream.   *Pagellus owenii*, Günther.
Pandora.   *Pagellus erythrinus* (Linn.).
Black Bream.   *Spondyliosoma cantharus* (Gmelin) =
   Cantharus lineatus, Day.
Bogue.   *Box boops* (Linn.) = *B. vulgaris*, Day.
Gilt-head.   *Sparus aurata*, Linn. = *Pagrus auratus*,
   Day.
Couch's Sea Bream.   *Pagrus pagrus* (Linn.) = *P.
   vulgaris*, Day.

LABRIDAE

Rainbow Wrasse.   *Coris julis*
   (Linn.).

Ballan Wrasse.   *Labrus bergylta*, Ascanius = *L. macu-
   latus*, Day.
Cuckoo Wrasse.   *Labrus mixtus*, Linn.
Gilt-head.   *Crenilabrus melops* (Linn.).
Gold-sinny.   *Ctenolabrus rupestris* (Linn.).
Scale-rayed Wrasse.   *Acantholabrus palloni* (Risso).
Rock Cook.   *Centrolabrus exoletus* (Linn.).

AMMODYTIDAE

Greater Sand Eel. *Ammodytes lanceolatus*, Lesauvage.
Lesser Sand Eel. *Ammodytes tobianus*, Linn.

TRACHINIDAE

Greater Weever. *Trachinus draco*, Linn.
Lesser Weever. *Trachinus vipera*, Cuvier and Valenciennes.

SCOMBRIDAE

Mackerel. *Scomber scombrus*, Linn.

Spanish Mackerel. *Pneumatophorus colias* (Gmelin)= *Scomber colias*, Day.
Tunny. *Thunnus thynnus* (Linn.)= *Orcynus thynnus*, Day.
Long-finned Tunny. *Germo alalunga* (Gmelin)= *Orcynus germo*, Day.
Bonito. *Katsuwonus pelamis* (Linn.)= *Thynnus pelamys*, Cuvier and Valenciennes.
Pelamid. *Sarda sarda* (Bloch)= *Pelamys sarda*, Day.
Plain Bonito. *Auxis rochei* (Risso).

XIPHIIDAE

Sword-fish. *Xiphias gladius*, Linn.

GOBIIDAE

Giant Goby. *Gobius capito*, Cuvier and Valenciennes.
Black Goby. *Gobius niger*, Linn.
Rock Goby. *Gobius paganellus*, Gmelin.

Fries's Goby. *Gobius friesii*, Malm.
Spotted Goby. *Gobius ruthensparri*, Euphrasen.

Painted Goby. *Gobius pictus*, Malm.
Common Goby. *Gobius minutus*, Gmelin.
Diminutive Goby. *Gobius scorpioides*, Collett.
Transparent Goby. *Aphia minuta* (Risso)=*A. pellucida*, Day.

CALLIONYMIDAE

Dragonet. *Callionymus lyra*, Linn.
Spotted Dragonet. *Callionymus maculatus*, Rafinesque.

BLENNIIDAE

Gattorugine. *Blennius gattorugine*, Bloch.
Montagu's Blenny. *Blennius montagui*, Fleming=*B. galerita*, Day.
Butterfly Blenny. *Blennius ocellaris*, Linn.
Shanny. *Blennius pholis*, Linn.

Yarrell's Blenny. *Chirolophis galerita* (Linn.)=*C. ascanii*, Day.

PHOLIDAE

Butter-fish. *Pholis gunnellus*, Linn. =*Centronotus gunnellus*, Day.

ZOARCIDAE

Viviparous Blenny. *Zoarces viviparus* (Linn.).

ANARHICHADIDAE

Cat-fish. *Anarhichas lupus*, Linn.

MUGILIDAE

Thick-lipped Grey Mullet. *Mugil chelo*, Cuvier.

Thin-lipped Grey Mullet. *Mugil capito*, Cuvier.

Golden Grey Mullet. *Mugil auratus*, Risso.

ATHERINIDAE

Sand Smelt. *Atherina presbyter*, Cuvier.

Order SCLEROPAREI

SCORPAENIDAE

Norway Haddock. *Sebastes marinus* (Linn.) = *S. norvegicus*, Day.

TRIGLIDAE

Tub-fish. *Trigla lucerna*, Linn. = *T. hirundo*, Day.
Red Gurnard. *Trigla cuculus*, Linn. = *T. pini*.

Grey Gurnard. *Trigla gurnardus*, Linn.
Piper. *Trigla lyra*, Linn.

COTTIDAE

Father Lasher. *Cottus scorpius*, Linn.
Long-spined Sea Scorpion. *Cottus bubalis*, Euphrasen.

Four-horned Cottus. *Cottus quadricornis*, Linn.

AGONIDAE

Armed Bullhead. *Agonus cataphractus* (Linn.).

CYCLOPTERIDAE

Lump-sucker. *Cyclopterus lumpus*, Linn.

LIPARIDAE

Sea Snail. *Liparis liparis* (Linn.) = *L. vulgaris*, Day.

Montagu's Sea Snail. *Liparis montagui* (Donovan).

GASTEROSTEIDAE

Three-spined Stickleback. *Gasterosteus aculeatus*, Linn.
Ten-spined Stickleback. *Pygosteus pungitius* (Linn.) = *Gasterosteus pungitius*, Day.
Fifteen-spined Stickleback. *Spinachia spinachia* (Linn.) = *Gasterosteus spinachia*, Day.

Order HETEROSOMATA

BOTHIDAE

Scald-fish. *Arnoglossus laterna* (Walbaum).

Turbot. *Scophthalmus maximus* (Linn.) = *Rhombus maximus*, Day.

Brill. *Scophthalmus rhombus* (Linn.) = *Rhombus laevis*, Day.
Megrim. *Lepidorhombus whiff-iagonis* (Walbaum) = *Arnoglossus megastoma*, Day.
Norwegian Topknot. *Phrynorhombus norvegicus* (Günther).
Eckstrom's Topknot. *Phrynorhombus regius* (Bonnaterre) = *Zeugopterus unimaculatus*, Day.

Common Topknot or Bloch's Topknot. *Zeugopterus punctatus* (Bloch).

PLEURONECTIDAE

Halibut. *Hippoglossus hippoglossus* (Linn.) = *H. vulgaris*, Day.

Long Rough Dab. *Hippoglossoides platessoides* (Fabricius) = *H. limandoides*, Day.

Dab. *Limanda limanda* (Linn.) = *Pleuronectes limanda*, Day.

Plaice. *Pleuronectes platessa*, Linn.

Lemon Sole. *Microstomus kitt* (Walbaum) = *Pleuronectes microcephalus*, Day.

Witch. *Glyptocephalus cynoglossus* (Linn.) = *Pleuronectes cynoglossus*, Day.

Flounder. *Platichthys flesus* (Linn.) = *Pleuronectes flesus*, Day.

SOLEIDAE

Sole. *Solea solea* (Linn.) = *S. vulgaris*, Day.

Sand Sole. *Pegusa lascaris* (Risso) = *Solea lascaris*, Day.

Thickback Sole. *Microchirus variegatus* (Donovan) = *Solea variegata*, Day.

Solenette. *Microchirus boscanion* (Chabanaud) = *Solea lutea*, Day.

Order PLECTOGNATHI

MOLIDAE

Sun-fish. *Mola mola* (Linn.) = *Orthagoriscus mola*, Day.

Truncated Sun-fish. *Ranzania truncata* (Retzius) = *Orthagoriscus truncata*, Day.

Order XENOPTERYGII

GOBIESOCIDAE

Cornish Sucker. *Lepadogaster gouani*, Lacepède.
Connemara Sucker. *Lepadogaster candollii*, Risso.
Two-spotted Sucker. *Lepadogaster bimaculatus* (Bonnaterre).

Small-headed Sucker. *Lepadogaster microcephalus*, Brook.

Order PEDICULATI

LOPHIIDAE

Angler. *Lophius piscatorius*, Linn.

Class MARSIPOBRANCHII
THE LAMPREYS   *PETROMYZONIDAE*

Three species of lamprey are found in British waters. All three venture some distance into fresh water and all three enter the sea, some species for a longer period than others. There are some authorities who are of the opinion that there is only one species of lamprey, the others being either dwarfs or immature specimens of the Sea Lamprey. The arrangement of the teeth and the suctorial discs, however, seem to belie this view.

The body is eel-like in shape and there are no scales, and it is remarkable for the sucker which replaces the normal mouth region of other fishes. There is a more or less circular, suctorial lip surrounding the teeth which are disposed as follows :

In the Sea Lamprey, *Petromyzon marinus* (Plate 1), there are two maxillary teeth set close together ; the tooth of the lower jaw is crescent shaped and has from seven to nine cusps ; on the tongue there are four ridged teeth placed in pairs ; on the inner side of the suctorial disc there are from seven to nine rows of sharp teeth, called 'suctorial teeth.'

In the Lampern, *Lampetra fluviatilis* (Plate 1), there is only one broad maxillary tooth ; the mandibular tooth has from six to nine cusps ; only one tooth on the tongue and the suctorial disc has an outer fringe of small teeth and within them are two rows of conical teeth with three large ones on each side.

The Brook or Planer's Lamprey, also known as the Pride, *Lampetra planeri*, has a similar dental arrangement to the lampern but the teeth generally are smaller and blunter.   This species very rarely visits the sea, but the other two spend far more of their time in the salt water than in the rivers.

The breathing arrangements of these lowly fishes are somewhat different from those in the true fishes. In the 'breathing chamber,' instead of gill-arches carrying numerous gill-filaments, there are gill-pouches (hence the class name—Marsipobranchii) of which there are seven on either side and each has its own canal-opening which connects it with the outside world. Although there is a single nostril on the top of its head it does not penetrate into the gill-basket, as the gill-chamber is called. In the closely related Hagfish the nostril does open into the gill-basket and this must be of great value to a fish which buries its head in the flesh of other fishes.

There is a strong resemblance to a third eye on the top of the head, too. The pineal gland is well developed and the tissue covering it is slightly transparent, especially in the adult. At one time in the distant past it is quite possible that the lampreys did have one or even two eyes on the top of their head in addition to the usual pair at the sides.

The food seems to consist of the flesh of other fishes and living ones at that. By means of the suctorial disc the lamprey can attach itself very firmly indeed to another fish and the teeth are ideally constructed for rasping chunks of its flesh off. Sometimes four or five of them will attack the one fish with what one could reasonably imagine to be fatal results.

The suctorial disc is also useful in obtaining a free ride; very often they will attach themselves to the side of a ship and so be carried to fresh hunting grounds.

Then there is another use to which this disc is put. When the lamprey enters the rivers to spawn (incidentally these rivers on the east coast are all south of the Wash) it may encounter strong currents and, although it is quite a powerful swimmer, it can obtain a welcome rest by sticking to a rock or some other solid body.

In February the male enters the rivers to spawn and here the disc comes in handy again. It proceeds to make a trough-like nest of stones which it lifts by means of the disc. Then the female arrives on the scene and lends a hand. If they should find a stone too heavy for one to manage then the two of them will struggle with it. When the nest is ready the female deposits her eggs in it and the male fertilizes them and an effort is made to cover them over. But by now they are exhausted and just drift with the tide. Some, perhaps, may reach the sea and so recover but there can be very few of them.

After quite a short time the young hatch out but they resemble their parents only in their eel-like shape. They are blind and they have no teeth (incidentally, the 'teeth' of the lamprey are not teeth at all, they are really horny structures which are replaced when they wear out), and they live in the mud like worms. In fact they look like worms. After a year, sometimes two, the young lamprey sets out for the sea, still not looking very much like its parents. At one time, indeed, they were thought to be a separate species and were given the name *Ammocoetes branchialis*.

The lampern spends more time in freshwater than does the foregoing species. In September to February the migration to the river starts, but nest-building operations commence in April and

May. Spawning exhausts this species also and it is doubtful if they ever reach the sea and survive.

The brook lamprey gets no nearer the sea than the brackish estuaries. It is the smallest of the three, having a length of no more than twelve inches. The lampern grows to a length of sixteen inches whilst the sea lamprey may exceed a length of three feet. All three species make excellent live bait for turbot and are useful as a whiffing bait for pollack and bass.

Class SELACHII

THE 'FALSE' SHARKS *LAMNIDAE*

The Selachians are fishes with cartilaginous skeletons (they harden with age usually) as distinct from the true fishes which have bony skeletons. The class is divided into two sub-classes, the Euselachii, the sharks and dogfishes, the skates and rays, and the Holocephali, the rabbit fishes. The rabbit fishes will not be dealt with here for they are comparatively rare and are only likely to be found off Iceland, the Shetlands and in deep water generally all along our west coasts.

Of the shark and dogfish kind, twenty-three species have been recorded from British waters but only about eleven of these can be considered as being either residents or fairly frequent visitors. The order to which they belong—the Pleurotremata—is divided into several families and the first of these to be discussed is the Lamnidae, three members of which will be mentioned, viz. the porbeagle, the thresher and the basking shark.

The Porbeagle, *Lamna cornubica* (Plate 4).

Only too frequently the fisherman will catch a porbeagle in his net when it can be a great nuisance, often breaking its way through, leaving a huge rent through which the rest of the catch will escape.

It may readily be recognized by its pointed snout and the keel-like ridge along each side of the tail, the two lobes of which are almost equal, an unusual thing in the sharks.

The teeth are lancet-shaped and seem to be designed more to hold their prey than to tear it. Mackerel, haddock, cod and whiting are favoured foods but the one most sought after is small dogfish; this, like the others, is swallowed whole.

The length may be up to ten feet and the weight is often considerable. In October 1889 some Folkestone fishermen caught a specimen nine feet three inches in length and weighing four and a half hundredweights and in 1892 the men in a Shoreham boat fishing for mackerel found themselves with a specimen in their net weighing five hundredweights and having a length of ten feet.

Large though they are, the body is of no commercial use. When a fisherman is unfortunate enough to capture one, all he can do is to make a peepshow of it and then sell the carcase for manure.

Mostly they are found off the Cornish coast in the summer time but they also travel along the south coast as far as the Thames Estuary and occasionally to the Wash. Their headquarters seem to be the Gulf of Gascony and the north coast of Spain. So far as is known they are viviparous.

Three or four years ago a lady sea angler in the West Country caught what was thought to be a record porbeagle. A photograph and details were sent to the U.S.A. to confirm it as being a world record, but to everybody's surprise it was shown to be a Mako Shark and not a porbeagle at all. Since then a number have been taken, so it is possible that some of the records of large porbeagles were of a shark hitherto unrecorded from British waters.

The Thresher Shark, *Alopias vulpes* (Plate 2). The most notable feature of this member of the Lamnidae family is the upper lobe of its tail, which is scythe-shaped and is remarkably long, and for this reason it is sometimes called the Sea Fox; the lower lobe is very short. In a specimen fifteen feet long (about the maximum length) the upper lobe will be about eight feet long. Incidentally, the weight of such a specimen would be around 550 pounds. Yet in spite of its size and vicious appearance this shark is relatively harmless.

Several theories have been put forward regarding the use to which this monstrous tail is put. Some think that it is used like a scythe to carve off lumps from the body of the mighty whale, but I think it is the killer whale (*Orca gladiator*) which has that unpleasant habit. A more likely use is to assist in rounding up the herrings and mackerel on which the shark feeds. My own opinion is that its main use is to enable the shark to turn quickly, a necessary feat when dealing with the speedy manœuvres of the wily mackerel.

Very little is known of its breeding habits but we do know that the egg, prior to being ejected, is similar to that of the dogfish, is about three inches in length (quite small for so large a fish), is of an amber colour and resembles a shell-less hen's egg. The summer is the egg-laying time for the thresher.

The headquarters of this shark are the sub-arctic regions, but it appears to visit most parts of our coast.

The Basking Shark, *Cetorhinus maximus* (Plate 2). This shark has been known by several names, including *Squalus maximus* and *Selache maxima*. At one time its chief claim to fame was just being something of interest to see to break up the monotony of an ocean voyage.

Centuries ago fishermen of the wild isles of Western Scotland and Ireland would risk their lives to capture one basking shark, sometimes being carried great distances out to sea whilst attached by harpoon and line to it. One-third of the creature (it weighs up to five tons or more with a length of up to thirty-five feet) is liver and most of that liver provides oil. The flesh would provide food for a number of people, the unused part being ground up for fertilizer, and the oil would provide a smoky sort of illumination.

When paraffin replaced oil as a luminant the basking shark had a break—until there came a demand for the liver oil for technical purposes. They were then hunted in earnest during the three months when they come close to the islands (May, June and July) doubtless because the plankton on which they feed is prolific in those parts at that time. Then the huge pancreas was found to be a useful source of insulin; this intensified the slaughter.

By way of a minor irritation, droves of sea lampreys will sometimes attach themselves to the shark's huge body.

Its travels seem to cover most of the northern seas with the northern part of the British Isles as its summer headquarters. It would seem from recent researches that the female, mature at 25 feet, produces one offspring at intervals of two years.

THE DOGFISHES   *SCYLIORHINIDAE*

Of the four 'dogfish' species found in British waters only two are at all common. Apart from the size—the Lesser Spotted Dogfish, *Scyliorhinus caniculus* (Plate 5), is from twenty to twenty-eight inches in length whilst the Larger Spotted Dogfish, *S. stellaris* (Plate 5), may attain a length of five feet—these two species differ considerably in respect of their spots. The former has numerous small spots scattered over its sides, the latter has only a few large spots.

The 'Lesser,' sometimes called the Rough Hound or Robin Huss, is oviparous, the eggs being laid in pairs and each egg contained in a tough, amber-coloured envelope. This envelope is partially transparent so that the baby dogfish within it is easily observable. Even the heartbeats are clearly visible as well as the occasional twitchings of the infant.

There is a pair of twining filaments at each end of the egg capsule, one pair of which protrudes from the oviduct of the female before the egg is extruded. She swims around a tangle of seaweed until the filaments become entangled in it, then she glides away leaving the egg behind. It is held by the weed until the young one is sufficiently developed to force its way out.

It is well distributed around our coasts and at times is present in vast numbers, to the disgust of the fishermen. At one time they were only landed when all other fish were scarce and fetched only a few pence a stone, being considered very poor fare indeed. Nowadays they command a reasonable price and the annual landings often exceed 150,000 hundredweights. Beheaded and skinned they can be seen as Rock Salmon on the fishmonger's slab or on the bill of fare of the fried-fish shop.

The skin is very rough indeed, as is the skin of numerous other members of the Selachii, and is used to this day by the cabinet-maker in place of sandpaper. The roughness is due to the unusual scales which consist of a base buried in the skin from which arises a backward-sloping spine. This type of scale or 'denticle' is also known as a dentoid or placoid scale and is probably the most primitive of the different scale types.

The mouth is crescent shaped and is situated on the underside of the head.

The Larger Spotted Dogfish, *S. stellaris* (Plate 5), sometimes known as the Nursehound or Bull Huss, is a less common species. Concerning this species Frank Buckland once wrote: 'They are vagabond curs of the ocean, that go prowling and snapping around anywhere and how for food.' This certainly seems to be the case; they grab what they can from the free-swimming population of the sea and when that source of food is scarce they use their long snouts to rout out molluscs and worms from the seabed.

They are well infested with parasites as, indeed, are most of the shark kind. Apart from intestinal parasites there are many external parasites, too, tiny relations of the shrimp and lobster kind—the parasitic copepods. Ten genera of these contribute towards making the life of the Nursehound a misery. Some genera provide species which attack only the mucous film surrounding the body and others attack the claspers, the intromittent organ of the male, and these must occasion considerable discomfort though still without really harming the well-being of the fish. But those which embed themselves in the gill-arches and which are usually called gill-worms actually tap the blood stream and eventually do considerable damage to their host.

THE TRUE SHARKS *CARCHARINIDAE*

With this family we enter into the domain of the true sharks, predatory and of quite large size.

Four species are recorded from our waters but of these the Hammerhead, *Sphyrna zygaena*, a sub-tropical species, has only been recorded three or four times.

The Blue Shark, *Carcharinus glaucus* (Plate 3), attains a length of twenty-five feet. It seems to arrive off the British coast in June, following the line of the Gulf Stream round Cornwall and up the Irish Sea to the west of Scotland and also to the west coast of Ireland. Herrings, pilchards and mackerel are its main objective and so rapacious is the pursuit that it even follows the fish into the fishermen's nets. Owing to the size and power of this shark this means that the net will be completely wrecked in the process for it does not seem to mind on what it exercises its scissor-like teeth. There is a rapidly growing number of shark anglers nowadays, based mainly on Looe and providing the local boatmen with a welcome addition to their incomes.

The colour of the back is a slaty blue, the under parts are white.

The Tope, *Eugaleus galeus* (Plate 4), otherwise known as the Toper, Penny Dog, Miller's Dog or Rig, is fairly common in the southern part of the British Isles, usually during the summer months; in some areas, however, especially the Thames estuary, they have been found in considerable numbers in November and December.

Of late years the angler has fished especially for them, often with very light tackle, and there can be little doubt that considerable skill is necessary in hooking and landing a large specimen. A length of seven feet has been given as being the maximum but there is a record of a nine-foot-long tope having been caught in 1847 off Maylandsea in the Black-water estuary in Essex.

It is a viviparous species and as many as thirty-two embryos have been found in one female.

The Smooth Hound, *Mustelus mustelus* (Plate 3), sometimes known as the Skate-toothed Dogfish, closely resembles the tope except for the disposition of the fins and the design of the teeth. In the Smooth Hound the latter are flat and arranged in a sort of mosaic, as also are those of the skate, and are ideal for crushing the molluscs and crustaceans on which both fishes feed.

The skin is smoother and softer than that of the sharks in general. Unlike most bottom-loving fishes it prefers clean, hard ground; consequently, although it is common near most parts of our coast, it avoids muddy estuaries as far as possible.

THE SPINY SHARKS   *SQUALIDAE*

Although ten species of this family have been found off Britain only two are not rare.

The family characteristics include the presence of only two dorsal fins and the absence of an anal fin. As they are surface swimmers there is no necessity for a nictitating membrane (a noticeable feature of many of the shark kind) on the eyes, consequently none are present.

There are two groups to this family and a representative of each is found in our waters. The members of the first group are powerful swimmers and so the upper lobe of the tail is well developed ; also, in this group, there is a spine in front of each of the dorsal fins. The members of the second group are of sedentary habit and so have a less efficient tail. There are no spines to the dorsal fins.

The Piked Dogfish, *Squalus acanthias* (Plate 5), belongs to the former group. At times it is even more abundant than the Lesser Spotted Dogfish, but only within recent years has it been generally sold to the public. On the Scottish coast, however, this fish has always been utilized. The flesh is eaten, oil is extracted from the liver and the offal consigned to the land as fertilizer. In Lancashire, too, it has been popular for a long time. Beheaded and skinned it is sold as Darwen Salmon, just as other dogfishes are sold as Rock Eel or Rock Salmon in the South of England.

Following the autumn mating, the young are born 'alive' in the spring at which season the females assemble in inshore waters. The length of the adult sometimes exceeds four feet.

The spines before the dorsal fins are particularly vicious and can inflict a wound which takes a long time to heal.

The Greenland Shark, *Somniosus microcephalus* (Plate 6). As the common name would suggest this shark inhabits the waters off the Greenland coast. Not uncommonly, however, specimens wander as far to the south as the Suffolk coast but it is off the Scottish coast that our largest Greenland sharks are caught. In 1895 one with a length of twenty-one feet was caught off May Island in the Firth of Forth.

There is a fallacy that these sharks hang together and slay whales but this is hardly likely, for they are of solitary, sluggish habit. Nevertheless, when they find a dead whale they will devour it voraciously. In the process of doing that they are oblivious of all other things, and on one occasion a specimen was so absorbed in its meal that even when repeatedly stabbed in the head it took no apparent notice at all.

There are two schools of thought regarding its eggs; one authority insists that it produces four young at a birth and yet another states that it deposits a number of small soft eggs, devoid of protective envelope or colouring, on the sea bed in deep water.

This ash-grey shark is utilized by the Greenlanders for several purposes. The liver of a large one will produce up to seventy gallons of oil, the flesh will be eaten, whilst the tough skin, cut into long strips and then joined end to end, is used as rope.

THE MONK FISHES   *SQUATINIDAE*
(Plate 7)

Only one member of this family, known also as the Fiddler or Angel Fish, inhabits our waters. In fact, our species, *Squatina squatina*, is found in very many parts of the world. It seems to be a connecting link between the dogfishes and the rays and so it is curious to speculate on the fact that there are only a very few species known. The implication seems to be that a big evolutionary jump was made in this section of the animal kingdom. Moreover, very few fossil species are known either.

It is very common at times round our coasts and often enters river estuaries, even the muddy ones. The larger specimens come from the deeper water where they may attain a length of five feet and a weight of half a hundredweight.

The skin, which is tough and durable, is of a blotched brownish-grey colour and was at one time used for covering sword handles and instrument cases. The flesh is not very much in demand owing to its coarse texture and strong ammonia flavour which varies according to the size and how the fish is cooked.

The method of feeding is of interest. Its food consists of flatfishes and whiting, fishes which can move much faster than it can itself, owing to its cumbersome build. Consequently, it has to attract its food to within range of its large mouth. This it does by lying on the seabed and agitating its fins so that the shrimps and worms which live there are disturbed. This brings the flatfishes and the whiting to the spot and also within striking distance of its jaws.

The Monk Fish is viviparous and as many as twenty-five infant monk fishes may be born at a time.

THE SKATES AND RAYS *RAJIDAE*

The skates and rays are all carnivorous but although at times they can move fairly quickly they are quite unfitted to chase after fast-moving creatures. Instead, they live mostly on the animals of the seabed, such as molluscs and crabs, organisms with which their specially designed mosaic-like teeth are well able to cope. Also, because their mouth is on the underside, they are able to capture swimming fishes by slithering over them.

Of the 150 or so known species twenty-one have been recorded from British waters, but of these only eight are either commonly resident or frequent visitors. All species lay eggs in the form of horny capsules and, so far as is known, the embryo may remain in the egg for up to a year before finally emerging The capsules, which, when empty, are common objects of the tide line, are rectangular in shape and have tendrils projecting from the corners, but these are not spiral as are those of the oviparous dogfishes.

All of the species have electric organs albeit by no means so powerful as those of the Electric or Torpedo Ray, *Torpedo marmorata*, specimens of which occasionally find their way into our waters from the warmer parts of the eastern Atlantic.

In all species the body is flattened, the tail attenuated and the mouth on the underside. There are two main divisions, those with long snouts (the skates) and those with short snouts (the rays).

THE LONG-NOSE RAYS

The Common Skate, *Raja batis* (Plate 8), is our most common species and the most sought after for the table. The largest specimen recorded from our waters measured just over seven feet across. Smaller ones, weighing up to fourteen pounds or so, are commonly caught in estuaries and offshore waters.

In common with the other rays, the mouth and

gill openings are on the under surface and the breathing holes, otherwise spiracles, are situated on the upper surface.

The Bottle-nose Ray, *R. marginata*, is also known as the White Skate, the Bordered Ray and the Burton Skate. It closely resembles the common skate but is of thicker build and is white on the underside and not grey or bluish. The younger specimens have an orange tint on the back with a distinct dark rim or border. The snout is sharply pointed. When fully grown they are the largest of our rays.

The only area where it seems to be at all common is the western part of the English Channel.

The Flapper Skate, *R. macrorhynchus*, is noted for its particularly long snout. There is such a strong similarity between it and the Common or Blue Skate that many authorities are of the opinion that it is merely a variety of that species. At one time its scientific name was *R. intermedius*, it being thought to be intermediate between the Common Skate and the Bottle-nose Ray. A number of specimens have been landed from the English Channel to as far east as Dover whilst on the French side and right round the coast to the Mediterranean it is extremely common.

The Shagreen Ray (*R. fullonica*), of similar appearance to the foregoing but with less pointed snout, comes into inshore waters in the summer as also does the Blonde Ray (*R. brachyura*) which may be recognized by its light fawn colour and numerous small black spots.

THE SHORT-NOSE RAYS

The Cuckoo Ray, *R. naevus*, is a species common to both the North and the Irish Seas. It may be readily recognized by the large and showy blotches at the bases of the two pectoral fins. These are black with yellow bands across their centres and a ring of yellow dots round the rims.

It prefers fairly deep water and so is ordinarily seen only by the trawler fishermen.

The Sandy Ray, *R. circularis*, is an inhabitant of the English Channel. It is of similar shape to the foregoing but without the blotches. Instead, the uniform sandy colour is broken up by numerous small white spots.

As with the other species of the rays there are distinct differences in the appearance of the two sexes. The male is armed with patches of claw-like spines on the upper side of the pectoral fins and in some species on the sides of the head also.

The Thornback Ray, *R. clavata* (Plate 9), commonly known as the Roker, is the commonest of the short-snouted rays and in many areas is caught at all seasons. Generally speaking, it comes inshore and up the estuaries to breed in early summer and moves to the deeper water in winter, but usually some remain behind to gladden the heart of the hardy cold-weather angler.

The colour is a mottled greyish brown and in the male there are four rows of hooked denticles along the back. Also there is a difference in the teeth, those of the male being pointed whilst those of the female are flat.

The species is generally common in the English Channel, the Irish Sea and the southern part of the North Sea but is not so common in the colder northern waters.

The Starry Ray, *R. radiata*, is one of the most spectacular looking of all the ray species. Its upper surface is studded with large plates armed with vicious backward-pointing spines. The female is the larger and also is more spiny than the male. The colder and deeper waters are its habitat, where it is by no means rare, but it has yet to be recorded from the English Channel.

The Spotted Ray, *R. montagui*, on the other hand is a more southern species and is quite common in the English Channel and round the Kent coast to the Thames. The colour of the upper surface is a deep brown and this is heightened by the numerous dark brown spots which cover it. The breeding habits are similar to those of the other rays.

THE STING RAYS   *TRYGONIDAE*

The Sting Rays are a tropical family, but there is one species which visits southern England in fair numbers in the autumn; in the spring, in the Thames estuary, there are numerous palm-sized specimens found in the shrimpers nets.

The Sting Ray, *Trygon pastinaca* (Plate 10), is the species in question and it is a species such as the fisherman could well do without catching. Right along the warmer southern shores of our islands the fisherman is liable to encounter them and even the larger specimens will enter the river estuaries at times.

The snout is very short, in fact, the body is of quite a round shape and the tail is long, slender and whip-like. About the middle of the tail is a long, sharp serrated spine which, with the tail flailing around, is capable of inflicting a severe and very painful wound; for this reason it is also known as the Fire or Fierce Claw. It has even been known to penetrate the toughest of seaboots. The ancient writers, Pliny in particular, insisted that there was poison in the sting, so painful and severe is the wound. Later scholars attributed this to the mucous and other matter entering the wound at the same time, but it is now known that a virulent venom is concealed at the base of the grooved spine.

When it is landed the fishermen cut the tail off first, as a safety measure, and then remove the liver which produces an oil which can be burned in lamps. The flesh is jettisoned. The spine may be cut out and used as a netting needle or for stringing flat fish together.

Unlike the other rays both this and the Eagle Ray are viviparous.

THE EAGLE RAYS   *MYLIOBATIDAE*

The Eagle Ray, *Myliobatis aquila*, has an even longer and more whip-like tail than has the foregoing. The tail has a poisonous spine, too, and this is situated behind the dorsal fin towards the end of the tail. When the fish is captured the tail lashes about like the tail of an angry cat. It is a cosmopolitan species with a distinct preference for the warmer waters where it attains quite a huge size. The largest species are the well-known 'devil' fishes of the deep-sea anglers.

The colour is a bronze green verging almost to black, according to the type of ground on which it is taken.

With the Eagle Rays there is a distinct move away from the other rays, inasmuch as the head region is distinct from the disc formed by the pectoral fins.

Class PISCES

THE STURGEONS   *ACIPENSERIDAE*

The Sturgeon (Plate 12), like the Salmon,
ascends the rivers to spawn and moves to the sea
where its food is. Sometimes it will travel up
river a considerable distance; it has even been
known to get as far up the Thames as Teddington
and the Trent as far as Nottingham.

Various species are found scattered over the seas
and rivers of the world, but the one which visits
the British Isles is the Common Sturgeon (*Acipenser sturio*), a native of the Baltic.

The body is considerably elongated and bears a
number of large bony scales or bucklers, five rows
of which run the length of the body. The tail is
unevenly forked, a reminder that it is not so very
far removed from the shark kind. The mouth is
on the underside of the head and bears four
barbels which must be of use in locating food. The
sturgeon routs about with its long snout in the sand
and mud of the seabed in search of the molluscs,
crustaceans and worms which form its principal
diet. The toothless mouth is like a telescopic
suction tube; the sand or mud is sucked in and the
unwanted material is spat out again.

The colour is a dusky green with a silvery
underside. Although the length may exceed
fourteen feet with a weight of two hundredweights
the eggs are very small, but as many as three
million may be found in the ovary of one female.
These eggs form the delicacy known as caviare
whilst from the swim-bladder the best quality
of isinglass is obtained. The flesh is highly
esteemed.

With the possible exception of the Salmon there has been more research into the life story of the herring than of any other British fish. The reason for this is fairly obvious because of its importance as a food fish. Yet, in spite of the intensity of these researches and the length of time they have been going on (intensively since 1920 and sporadically during the past hundred years), there are many important points on which we are still very much in the dark. For example, although we can tell within a little when and where the annual migrations will take place for spawning purposes, we cannot predict with any certainty where the spawning grounds will be.

Also, the divergences in the breeding seasons from one place to another has led investigators to the conclusion that there are two distinct races of herring. The Sea or Autumn Herring is the one fished for by the fishermen on the east coast of Scotland and, later in the year, by the East Anglian drift-netters. Off Norway and in the Baltic the kind fished for is the Spring or Coastal Herring, sometimes called the Baltic Herring.

The Herring, *Clupea harengus* (Plate 13) itself is a soft-finned fish, bluish-green on the upper surface and silver on the underside. The eggs, 30,000 per female, have a diameter of between 0.92 mm. and 1 mm. and are unusual among surface-living food fishes as being demersal. The eggs are laid on shingly ground where they frequently become attached to clumps of 'whiteweed' as the fishermen call the Hydroid colonies. At other times the currents carry them into the channels in deepish water where they have been known to accumulate in vast masses weighing several hundredweights.

The young herrings move from the sea to the shallow water and into river estuaries. In the Thames, they travelled as far up-river as Blackwall in the days when pollution was far less rife than it is at present. After at least six months in their shallow water nurseries the young herrings (they are known as 'sild' in Scandinavian countries) move into the deeper water and seem to vanish from our ken until they appear in the adult shoals. They are mature at about four years of age.

The Sprat, *C. sprattus* (Plate 11), is a distinct species of fish and is not, as many suppose, merely a young herring. The two species differ in several marked respects which are discernible even in the young stage when, all mixed up, they form the whitebait which is so highly esteemed by the epicure. Here it should be noted that the whitebait is not a distinct species of fish; it consists in the Thames estuary of the young of the herring and sprat and in other places of sand eels and other small fishes.

In the herring the pelvic fins are very slightly behind the commencement of the dorsal fin, in the sprat they are in front of it. Moreover, in the sprat there is a ridge of strong spines between the pelvic fins and the tail along the belly; in the herring these spines are neither strong nor sharp.

The eggs are pelagic, floating on or near the surface, and spawning occurs from January to June in the English Channel. Then the sprat seeks deeper water and seems to travel right round the British Isles to reappear off Norway where it forms a summer fishery. On the other hand they might be local races. In the autumn it migrates towards the east coast of England, arriving off Suffolk in October or thereabouts. Then, in November, either early or late, it shoals off the mouth of the Thames where it forms an important fishery. It is canned under the title of 'Brisling'; the term 'Sardine' is reserved for the small canned pilchards.

The Pilchard, *Sardina pilchardus* (Plate 11). This is a larger fish than the foregoing, having a length of about nine and a half inches. Also, its scales are considerably larger. Another important difference is in the relative position of the dorsal fin, it being some distance in front of the pelvic fin.

The pilchard is a southern fish and is particularly common off the coasts of Spain and France. In Cornish waters great shoals regularly appear and give rise to a considerable fishery, but they are a rare fish elsewhere in Britain though sometimes quite large shoals will venture to the north as they do on occasions to the Thames estuary.

Spawning takes place throughout the whole of the English Channel and western approaches, and the eggs can be recognized without any great difficulty. Between the yolk and the membrane or 'skin' of the egg there is a large space, known as a perivitelline space, a feature also found in the egg of the Long Rough Dab. But the yolk of the pilchard's egg is also divided into segments and has a small oil globule; no other fish found in our waters has eggs with all three characteristics.

The approved and age-old method of cooking the pilchard is known as scowling; the fish are split open like a kipper, peppered and placed flat, one on the other, with the backs outside, and roasted on a gridiron.

The Allis Shad, *Alosa alosa* (Plate 12), also one

of the great herring clan, is a fish of the large southern estuaries, the Severn and the Shannon and formerly of the Thames where at times it is still occasionally seen. Like the salmon, it moves from the sea to the rivers to spawn and travels as far up river as pollution will allow. In some Continental rivers this is almost to the source.

In India and the U.S.A. various species of shad are raised on fish farms in a big way and form an important food item, but although many years ago our two species formed extensive fisheries they are not much bothered with nowadays. This, one would assume, is because the flesh is insipid and only too liberally endowed with bones.

The Twaite Shad, *Alosa finta* (Plate 16), differs from the Allis in two marked ways. It has a row of distinctive dark dots along the sides, whilst the gill rakers which act as sieves in capturing the minute organisms which form part of its diet are shorter and less numerous than in the allied species.

The distribution, although more or less confined to the southern half of the British Isles, is more general; the Twaite does not go so far up-river to breed. Nevertheless, the breeding habits of the two are much the same and the eggs are only very slightly heavier than their surrounding medium. Consequently, although strictly speaking they are demersal, sinking to the sea bed, they float just above the bottom and so can be carried about by the tides without getting injured.

In some Octobers anglers on Southend pier make quite large catches of this shad, some individuals being fifteen or more inches in length.

The Anchovy, *Engraulis encrasicholus* (Plate 11), is another fish which has a distinctive egg, the only oval pelagic egg to be found in our waters.

Ordinarily, it is considered as being a Mediterranean and Atlantic fish yet one of its greatest spawning grounds is in the Zuyder Zee area and the Schelde estuary. The fish enter the Dutch breeding grounds in spring where they spend the summer and spawn. Then, during autumn and early winter, they return down the English Channel and so travel to the Atlantic. After their second year of spawning they travel farther than after the first. So far no specimens have been found with scales showing a third year growth so it would seem that their extensive travels exhaust their vitality at an early age.

Sometimes a fair number of anchovies are caught by the spratters off the Kent coast and by the Dover drift-netters, otherwise they are only found as scattered individuals. Some years ago I found a single specimen on the beach just north of Lowestoft. Presumably it had been caught by a shore angler and thrown away in disgust. The length was four and a half inches and it was easily recognizable by the deep cleft of the mouth.

THE SALMON KIND   *SALMONIDAE*

The Salmon, *Salmo salar* (Plate 17). Although this fish is more commonly known from the rivers, it is really a sea fish. Like the shad, it enters the rivers for the sole purpose of spawning; in the sea it feeds, develops and grows, but whereas there are few secrets about its life whilst in freshwater, its life in the sea is almost a closed book. Salmon are rarely caught in the trawl and it would seem they swim singly and at a depth at which the trawls do not usually operate.

When they return from the sea they are fat and lusty despite the 'lice' with which they are infested. After a few days in freshwater the sea lice die off but the salmon does not remain unmolested for long; an even larger crop of parasites infests it and on top of all a serious disease awaits it if it should suffer the slightest scratch or abrasion. A bacillus attacks such injuries, causing a patch of mortifying flesh and on this a fungus develops similar to the familiar 'cotton wool' disease which causes considerable mortality among goldfishes.

The young salmon spends the first two years of its life in the rivers as a parr and the next year prior to descending to the sea as a smolt. At three years it is called a grilse. Such grilse as enter the rivers to spawn return to the sea as grilse kelts. After spending more than one winter in the sea it is called a 'salmon.'

Sea Trout, *Salmo trutta* (Plate 20). The Sea Trout has similar habits to the salmon except that it has a greater predilection for freshwater and even when it goes to the sea it tends to remain in the vicinity of river estuaries. Also, it feeds whilst in the freshwater, a thing the salmon rarely does.

Just as the trout of the rivers is remarkably influenced by its environment—giving rise to a great number of varieties, each with distinct characteristics—so the trout from the various estuaries round the coast vary. Thus the Peal of Devon and Cornwall, the Sewen of South Wales, the White Trout of Ireland and elsewhere the Salmon Trout, like the freshwater species, are all varieties of the one species—*Salmo trutta*.

The Smelt, *Osmerus eperlanus* (Plate 16), otherwise the Sparling and popularly referred to as the cucumber fish, from its unmistakable cucumber smell. Certain old fishermen of my acquaintance insist that these fish reside permanently in the estuaries and in the summer bed down in the muddy holes. True, they are to be found in some estuaries in greater or lesser numbers at all seasons, but the time when they are really prolific is during the eight months from September to May according to the locality. During their season, many, many years ago, they formed an important fishery.

The eggs are demersal and adhesive and of a pale yellow colour. A fully grown adult will have a length of up to eight inches or so and its colour during life is as delightful as that of any other fish.

THE EELS   *ANGUILLIDAE*

Of the numerous species of eels only two are common in our waters and only on rare occasions do specimens of the other species visit us.

The Common Eel, *Anguilla anguilla* (Plate 1), is perhaps the better known of the two species, principally because it inhabits all types of still or slow-moving waters, as well as the estuaries. Moreover, its amazing life story has been studied intensively and written about voluminously during the past sixty or seventy years.

Briefly its story is that towards the time when the irresistible urge comes to breed it moves from pond, stream or ditch to the nearest river mouth, sometimes making the journey overland, generally when the grass is heavy with dew. After a sojourn in the estuary where the somewhat saline

water doubtless prepares it for its subsequent
journey to the deep mid-ocean water where it will
breed and die, it proceeds to an area somewhere
between the Azores and the Bahamas. Here the
eggs are laid and fertilized.

At first the baby eels do not in the least resemble
the adults—they grow to a length of about four to
five inches, are flattened from side to side and are
sufficiently transparent for the 'innards' to be seen.
The eyes are relatively huge and resemble large
blobs of quicksilver. But by the time the babies
have reached their home shore they will have
shrunk considerably and adopted the round shape
of the adult and lost their transparency.

In some estuaries, particularly that of the Severn,
the elvers, as the young eels are called, arrive in
vast numbers and are collected and transported to
waters far away, even to Holland, where they will
develop to a sufficient size to suit the requirements
of the jellied-eel merchants.

Incidentally, although the eel when cooked is
wholesome and highly nutritious, its blood plasma
is poisonous.

The Conger Eel, *Conger conger* (Plate 21), is
essentially a marine species but its breeding habits
are very much the same as those of the common eel.
There is, however, a distinct possibility that its
larval development is not completed until it nears
the continental shelf, for the leptocephali or larvae
are occasionally found near our coast and once I
captured two very lively specimens whilst trawling
off the Thanet coast in 1933.

It is also possible that some of the spent adults
return to the inshore waters after spawning. I
base this assumption on the fact that not infrequently huge congers—seven feet or more in

length and with a girth like that of a man's thigh—
are stranded on the shore. The flesh of such
giants is usually flabby and watery when cooked
and utterly lacking in the fine flavour of the
ordinary kind.

THE SAURY PIKES *SCOMBERESOCIDAE*

The Skipper or Saury, *Scomberesox saurus* (Plate
14), is the only member of this queer-looking
family in our fauna. Because of its strong
resemblance to the related Garfish their differences
should be noted first. The teeth of the saury are
very much smaller and its beak-like mouth is
shorter than in the garfish. The rays of the
dorsal and anal fins of the garfish are all connected
by membrane whereas the hinder end of those
same fins in the saury is broken up into separate
small rays. Also, it is a shorter fish, having a
maximum length of about eighteen inches.

The saury comes into the Channel from the
warmer parts of the Atlantic in shoals which keep
to the inshore waters, swimming near the surface
in swift dashes reminiscent of its near relation the
flying fish. Occasionally, shoals will travel as far
north as the Firth of Forth and some have been
taken in the Irish Sea.

The eggs are laid near the surface in the open
sea in the warmer parts of the Atlantic. They are
small and bear filaments and these probably help
them to float near the surface. A curious feature
of the young saury is its mouth—the elongated
jaws do not develop for some months, the lower
'beak' appearing first.

THE GARFISHES

BELONIDAE

(Plate 14)

This fish, of which we have only one British species, *Belone belone*, is perhaps best known for the strange fact that its bones are green even when it is cooked. For this reason the average housewife, quite unnecessarily, fears that it might be poisonous to eat. In fact, it makes very good eating indeed.

It has various local names, viz. Sea Pike, Gorebill, Longnose, Greenbone, Hornfish, Sea-needle, Old Wife and numerous others and this gives rise, at times, to some confusion.

In the spring it moves into the shallow waters to spawn, at which times it precedes the mackerel and for this reason is sometimes known as the 'mackerel guide.' The eggs are covered with small, sticky filaments with which they adhere to stones and other solid objects.

The young gars remain in the shallows throughout the summer and then, in company with their elders, move into the deeper water for the winter. Although the larvae have prominent beaks these do not properly develop for some months, the lower one becoming elongated first and this gives them a most unusual appearance. Frequently these needle-like fry—about two inches in length—are found in the whitebait catch.

The adults of this rapacious and destructive species are not very much sought after by the professional fisherman, although there was once a limited special fishery for them in the Blackwater estuary in Essex. The angler, on the other hand, considers their early arrival a good omen for the bass fishing later.

THE PIPE FISHES   *SYNGNATHIDAE*
(Plate 15)

These are amongst the most unusual of the British fishes, not only for their elongated snake-like shape and the curiously elongated head which so much resembles that of a horse that one species is called the Sea Horse, but also for the pouch on the male's abdomen into which the eggs are deposited by the female.

The body of these fishes is encased in a series of jointed bony rings—that being the form the scales take. Thus, although the fish is encased in armour, that armour is flexible. The Sea Horse is the exception.

They have an unusual way of swimming; sometimes they are perpendicular with either the head or the tail uppermost; sometimes horizontal. Progress generally is slow and the fish only just maintains its position in the water, but when it wants to move more rapidly it writhes and turns like a wounded snake.

The food consists almost entirely of tiny crustaceans and in the pursuit of them the head is continuously on the move, the long snout poking and peering into clumps of weed and sea-moss. The victim is cautiously approached until the mouth is only a few inches away, then the fish sucks the crustacean in, puffing its cheeks out in the process.

Including the Sea Horse there are seven species found in our waters and although they are all superficially alike a closer inspection will reveal striking differences in the shape of the head, the mouth and the disposition of the fins.

They are not unpalatable to eat when cooked but their lack of flesh, even in the larger specimens, is a drawback. Other fishes, though, are very much averse to their flesh and even when cut up and mixed with other food sea fishes in the aquarium will reject them.

Two species are particularly common; they are the Great Pipe-fish, *Syngnathus acus*, and the Broad-nosed Pipe-fish *Siphonostoma typhle*. The former will grow to a length of eighteen inches whilst the latter rarely attains more than thirteen inches. Their range is from northern Norway to the English Channel, fairly close inshore. The fry are pelagic and are often caught in the plankton net. Spawning takes place in early spring and although the fry seem to be entirely independent of their parents they will retreat to the brood pouch of the male at the slightest hint of danger.

These two species differ, apart from the relative size, in the more robust snout of *S. typhle* and its more whip-like tail.

The Snake Pipe-Fish, *Entelurus aequoreus*, and the other Nerophis species come into the English Channel from the Atlantic. The caudal fin is remarkably small and has only six rays and in the Straight-nosed Pipe-fish, *Nerophis ophidion*, this fin is entirely absent. The Worm Pipe-fish is even more attenuated and this is accentuated by the small dorsal fin. The two last-named fishes are rarely found in the trawl except when trapped in a mass of weed. *Syngnathus rostellatus* occasionally visits these shores but it is only a few inches in length. At various times I have captured specimens in the plankton net in the Thames estuary.

One of our most interesting fishes is a close relative of the Pipe-fishes. It is the Sea Horse, *Hippocampus hippocampus* (Plate 15), the habitat of which is centred in the laminarian zone of the Bay of Biscay, where it is quite common. Frequently, however, it is found off Cornwall, the Channel Islands and even along the whole length of the south-east and south-west coasts. As a rule they are only seen as dried curios on the mantel-piece in the fisherman's cottage. When seen in the living state they are even more remarkable looking. The eyes, which are yellow, can move independently of each other and they seem always to be on the move, searching among the weeds for the tiny entities on which it feeds. When it swims it does so in an upright position, moving in a jerky manner. More often than not, the sea horse remains stationary with the prehensile tail wrapped round the stem of a seaweed.

THE HAKES   *MERLUCCIIDAE*

Although the Hake (Plate 18), a close relation of the cod, principally inhabits the deeper waters it is a familiar sight on the fishmonger's slab. At times, it has been captured in inshore waters, those off Dover and Harwich in particular.

It is a fish of distinctive shape, with a deeply cleft mouth admirably suited to deal with the herrings and mackerel on which it voraciously feeds when in shallower water or the Gadoid Poutassou and squid in the open sea. The colour is white on the underside and a brownish-slate colour on the back with dark spots. The mouth is black and the fins also are outlined in black. The teeth are long and sharp and with these the hake wreaks havoc amongst the pilchard shoals off the Cornish coast. Admiralty charts see the 'soundings' (i.e. the portion of the seabed which adheres to the tallow of the sounding lead) given as consisting of hake's teeth but these are not the teeth of the fish in question, although there is a slight resemblance in size and shape. They are really the shells of the Tooth Shell (*Dentalium*) which abound at the entrance to the English Channel between the Channel Islands and Cornwall and it is here, and along the south coast of Ireland that the hake is most abundant.

Spawning takes place in summer, but as this fish seems to be of a restless nature, both as an adult and as a fry, the grounds vary from time to time. Even the stratum of water at which it swims will vary; sometimes the shoals will be near the surface and at others near the bottom. Sometimes the spawning grounds will be off the west coasts and sometimes off Jutland. The eggs are minute, about one-twenty-fifth of an inch in diameter, but the adult may achieve a length of up to two feet and a weight of twenty pounds. There are only two dorsal fins as against the three of the cod.

THE COD KIND   *GADIDAE*

At least fifteen different species of this valuable group of fishes frequent British waters, but only about half a dozen of them are likely to be seen in the shops. This is only because most of the others are either too small or not sufficiently common to warrant a separate fishery.

They fall into four divisions, roughly, viz. those with three dorsal fins and two anal fins—Cod, Haddock, Bib, Poor Cod, Coal-fish (all the foregoing have barbels) and the Whiting and Pollack (without barbels); those with two dorsal fins, the front one the shorter, and one anal fin—Ling,

Fork-beard and, in freshwater, the Burbot; the Rocklings, as the foregoing, but with barbels on both the upper and lower jaws and the front dorsal fin narrow; then there is the Torsk, with only one anal and dorsal fin both of which are long.

The Cod, *Gadus callarias* (Plate 24), is perhaps the most popular and numerous of all the northern fishes. It is not found nearer the equator than 40 degrees north and is principally found between 50 and 75 degrees north to a depth of 120 fathoms. The only time they approach the coast, other than as single individuals, is when they shoal at breeding time in January.

The length may be from two to four feet with a weight of up to one hundred pounds. The colour varies according to the locality—thus in the North Sea it is usually greenish or brownish-green with a number of brown or yellow spots, towards the Faroes the colour darkens and generally there are no spots, and farther north still, off Greenland. Iceland and the north coast of Norway it often has a large patch of black on the sides. I am of the opinion that this colour variation is not so much due to environment as to separate races living in definite areas.

The cod is one of the few true fishes with a liver of any commercial value. The halibut is another.

One of its greatest enemies is the Myxine or Hag-fish, that lowly, eel-like and hermaphrodite relation of the lamprey which attaches itself to its victims and eats away all their insides and for this reason is sometimes called the Devourer.

A young cod is called a codling and I am frequently asked, 'When does a codling cease to be a codling and become a cod?' The point is, of course, it is a cod all the time, right from when it is born and it all boils down to a question of size. The age can only be determined by a close examination of the fish itself. There are two principal methods of ascertaining this, and with the cod and certain other species, three. The scales show growth rings, very similar to the annular growth rings of the tree, and in the skull there is a pair of small, oval bones of ivory-like composition situated loosely in small pits; these, too, bear similar yearly growth rings.

Of late years it has been discovered that some species of fish, especially the cod, reveal a similar structure in the rays supporting the dorsal fins. These bony structures are sliced through transversely with a tiny circular saw—the sharpest of razors will distort them—and the section embedded in paraffin wax or plasticine and examined under a low power with the microscope.

The Haddock, *Gadus aeglifinus* (Plate 24). One of the most commercially valuable of our native fishes is the haddock, highly esteemed for its delicate flavour, whether cured or fresh. It inhabits the deeper waters from the very north of the British Isles to the south and has even been captured by anglers as near to the heart of London as Dagenham Reach and in March 1879 some were taken at Purfleet.

Spawning occurs from five miles or so off the east coast of Scotland from February to April and the eggs resemble those of the cod but are slightly larger, about one-twentieth of an inch in diameter. Also, they are buoyant as are the eggs of the other members of the cod family, with the exception of the Burbot. In the larvae, as in those of the cod, black is the predominant colour although in the species in question it is confined to the lower edge of the body. With age the black pigment becomes concentrated into the familiar black blotches on either side of the shoulder region.

In the matter of feeding the adult is less of a predatory nature than is the cod and the principal food consists of echinoderms, shrimps, various types of mollusc including octopus and cuttlefish as well as bivalves and univalves. Hermit crabs, swimming crabs and sand-hoppers also are devoured. Numerous species of marine worm are sought out, but by far the most favoured of all is the curious worm known as the Sea Mouse (*Aphrodite*).

Although Day records an amazing specimen from Dublin Bay which had a length of thirty-seven and a half inches and a weight of twenty-four and a quarter pounds, the largest, out of a very large number, measured by the Scottish Fishery Board was twenty-five inches in length.

The Bib, *G. luscus* (Plate 19). This fairly common fish is also known as the Pout, Whiting Pout, Whiting Wule, Bragay and, because it goes 'off' so rapidly after being caught, sometimes as the 'Stink alive.' Yet when it is cooked immediately after being captured it eats excellently.

When it is first caught it has a beautiful iridescent copper colouring with dark cross-bands and a black spot at the fore end of each pectoral fin. But within half an hour or so the colour becomes a dull, lifeless brown. The baby Bibs are readily recognized because the rear third of the body is colourless.

It is a more southern fish than either of the foregoing and even enters the Mediterranean. Spawning takes place well off-shore in the English Channel from January to April, the fry very soon moving towards the shallower coastal waters. The adults are at their most prolific in the estuaries and all along the south coast during the summer, but they are captured by anglers at most times of the year. The maximum weight is five pounds.

The Poor Cod, *G. minutus* (Plate 19). This common species is a slender edition of the Bib and is smaller generally, rarely exceeding eight and a half inches in length. It does not possess black bands and the colour is a brownish yellow on the back. It is found all round our coasts but the spawning grounds are off the south and west coasts in fairly deep water where, from March to June, the tiny eggs are laid. After passing the larval stage the young move into inshore waters where they seem to feed mostly on shrimps. A fair number come up in the trawl and many fishermen are of the opinion that they are Bibs, but there are numerous distinct differences as a reference to the illustrations will show.

The Whiting, *G. merlangus* (Plate 26). This is one of our commonest inshore fishes and is probably the most delicate tasting of all the cod family. The flesh, too, is delicate and it suffers as much as, if not more than, the mackerel from packing and carriage; consequently it, too, should be cooked as soon after capture as possible.

Although the North Sea seems to possess the greatest concentration of whiting the largest specimens come from the coasts of Devon and Cornwall where they run to three or even four pounds in weight. Around Dartmouth the fishermen dry them in the sun and they are then known as 'buckthorn' and, as such, are considered by many people as being superior to the fresh fish. Along the quayside at Dieppe I have seen whiting being filleted in the fish sheds at an incredible speed. The fillets are packed in boxes and are in the Paris markets within a few hours of being landed.

Off Plymouth spawning takes place a few miles off shore from February onwards, but farther north it is delayed by a month or six weeks. At first the baby whiting possesses a barbel but this gradually disappears with age. In the adult the sides are silvery and there is a black spot at the upper fore end of the pectoral fin.

In the matter of food it is very greedy and not very discriminating, a point which pleases the angler considerably. Young fish are eaten, including young members of its own species, pink and brown shrimps and other small crustacea and, occasionally, worms and molluscs such as tellina and the cockle. When mature it measures eight inches in length.

Coal-fish, *G. virens* (Plate 22). The body of this fish which may attain a length of forty or more inches is slender and, on the upper part, of a blue-black colour, becoming darker with age. The lateral line is white. One of its common names is 'coley' (the French name is '*colin*') whilst in some places it is known as saithe or sillock. Of recent years it has enjoyed an increased popularity in the fish shops, but personally I find the flesh somewhat coarse both in texture and palate.

The adults feed voraciously on other fishes and, in particular, on the herring in the North Sea.

The spawning season is from February to April and later in the year, at a length of about an inch, the fry swarm around rocky shores amongst the waving seaweeds or in harbours. At this stage the diet consists of such crustaceans as are found amongst the weed or on the bottom. At a year old the length may be between four and seven inches and after that they leave the shallow waters and proceed to the deeper waters far from the land. With age, too, the coal-fish undergoes some slight changes—the upper jaw, which is longer than the lower one in the yearlings, becomes the shorter one and the barbel becomes rudimentary.

The Pollack, *G. pollachius* (Plate 26). Like the coal-fish, the pollack is found from Norway to the Mediterranean, but whereas the former is more common on the northern coasts, the pollack is at its most prolific along the south coast. Also it prefers water that is less deep and has not been found at a greater depth than forty fathoms.

Spawning, generally, occurs a month or so later than with the coalfish except off Devon and Cornwall where it may occur as early as February. The habits and food of the young are similar and the adults are almost exclusively fish eaters and prefer sprats, gurnard, sand eels and scaldfish.

It is difficult to discuss this fish without also referring to the coal-fish, for the two are so very similar in so many respects. The colour, however, is of a brownish hue and the lower jaw is even more prominent.

The sea angler and, in particular, the angler who fishes the western part of the English Channel and the southern part of the Irish Sea, finds the pollack a worthy adversary. It is game and strong and attains quite a useful weight—an eight-pounder is by no means unusual.

Because of its abundance off the south-west peninsula, the naturalists at the Marine Laboratory at Plymouth adopted this fish as a guinea-pig for their fish experiments. For instance, in the course of their researches on the smelling powers of fishes, they found that the pollack did not seem to smell its food at all, at least, when it was hungry. It has been known to gulp down clams that have been soaked in turpentine, alcohol, chloroform and other unappetizing substances. On the other hand, blind specimens have been observed to seek out their food by smell alone, but this does not prove anything. It is just a case of necessity.

The Greater Fork-beard, *Urophycis blennoides* (Plate 18). This oceanic fish migrates to the south-west of Britain and the North Sea in the winter. It so closely resembles the hake both as regards the shape and disposition of the fins and the shape of the head that it is sometimes known as the Forked Hake or as the Hake's Dame. From the chin there hangs a barbel whilst the pelvic fins are concentrated into two long filaments which extend for nearly the whole length of the fish. Although it has been known to attain a length of two feet, owing to its scattered appearances the Greater Fork Beard has no commercial value, but it does make good eating.

The Ling, *Molva molva* (Plate 28) is a most interesting fish in several respects. It is a long, narrow fish with an average length of four to six feet with seven feet as about the maximum. Although the usual colour is a uniform grey in the adult (some may have scattered black spots over the sides) that of the young ones is particularly striking; there is an olive-brown band along the sides whilst across the body for its entire length there are black bands. When the fish is about a foot in length the bands break up into black blotches and as it grows larger these gradually merge into the general drab colour scheme of the adult.

The eggs are very small, about one-twenty-fifth of an inch in diameter and each contains one large pale-green oil globule. Spawning takes place in early summer.

The flesh is esteemed by many people, especially those in the north of Scotland. It is of a fine texture resembling that of turbot. The oil from the liver was formerly used as fuel for their lamps by the poorer people whilst half a fluid ounce taken in a glass of beer was considered as being an effective cure for rheumatism. The liver itself is reckoned as being quite a dainty by some people and in the places where the ling is sold fresh a portion of the liver is given to the purchaser to provide the oil to fry his fish in.

The food consists almost entirely of other fishes, and those who fish for ling with lines bait their hooks with pieces of mackerel, herring or haddock. But ordinarily they will hunt most other fishes, including young salmon.

THE ROCKLINGS   *GADIDAE*

Of the eight or so known species of Rockling, three are found in British waters. The young of all three species are silvery in colour and are known as 'Mackerel Midges.' Sometimes they are found far out to sea swimming in huge shoals near or on the surface where they are relentlessly pursued by mackerel which, in their turn, may be pursued by porpoises.

The dorsal fin in all species consists of a single, long narrow fin in front of which, and extending to just behind the head, is a deep groove and in this there is a membrane, protruding just a little bit above the groove. No one seems to know why it should have this membrane but it has been noticed that even when all the fins are at rest the membrane quivers violently.

All have minute scales covering the body.

In the Three-bearded Rockling, *Onos tricirratus* (Plate 23), sometimes known as the Whistle Fish, there are two barbels on the upper lip protruding forwards, as indeed do these barbels in the other two species, and one on the lower lip. It averages about fifteen inches in length and is a deep yellowish-brown colour with large spots over the body of a deeper shade. The adults keep to shallow water, preferably where it is rocky.

The range is from southern England to the Mediterranean but it does enter the North Sea and has been found as far to the north as Norway.

The Five-bearded Rockling, *Onos mustelus* (Plate 23), has a pair of barbels in front of the nostrils and another pair on the upper lip and one on the chin. It is a slightly larger species than the foregoing and not uncommonly attains a length of eighteen inches. It is also a more common fish and is found on most parts of the British coast. The colour is brownish and I have seen them with a bronze lustre. There are no dark patches on the body.

Mr. Couch, the author one hundred years ago of a large work on British fishes, refers to the nest made by this species. He stated that the nest was made of corallines thrust into a crevice in the rocks but instead of the eggs being deposited in it like those of the stickleback they are scattered through the mass of coralline. Although this fish is common in the Thames estuary, where there is an abundance of whiteweed and coralline, I have yet to hear of such a nest from the shrimpers there. Nor have I heard of one being found elsewhere. It was probably the nest of a wrasse.

The food of this species seems to consist of amphipods, shrimps and small crabs. Although the flesh is quite palatable it does not appear to be used as food.

The Four-bearded Rockling, *Onos cimbrius* (Plate 22), is a smaller and more stream-lined species than the other two. It is more slender and has not their up-thrust head. The habitat is more northerly, too, extending from the British Isles to Norway. There are three barbels on the upper lip and one on the lower. The colour is similar but there are no spots. The eggs are small and have a single oil globule and resemble those of its congeners.

The Lesser Fork-beard, *Raniceps raninus*, otherwise known as the Tadpole-fish, because of its queer shape, was at one time considered as being the rarer of the two Fork-beard species found in our waters. But there are several records of its being found off the Kent and Essex coasts as well as from off Cornwall and the rocky coastal waters of the north.

The pectoral and dorsal fins are quite long and the head is flattened and frog-like. The colour is dark brown, except for the lips and they are white. The scales in both species are small.

Finally, in this account of the Cod family, there is the Torsk or Tusk, *Brosme brosme*, a species with one barbel only and that is on the chin. A valuable food fish, it has a length of up to three feet, and it is found in fair numbers off the north British coast. There is no record, so far as I know, of its being found south of the Wash. It is probably a sub-Arctic species and, as it swims at a depth of from 100 to 300 fathoms, is unlikely to be seen by the angler other than on the fishmonger's slab in northern towns. The scales are small, the head and eyes particularly large.

THE OPAH   *LAMPRIDIDAE*

The only representative of this family found in British waters is the truly magnificent Opah, *Lampris luna* (Plate 25), otherwise known as the King-fish, Sun-fish, Sea Pert or Jerusalem Haddock.

The colouring of the living fish is quite spectacular. The upper part is purple, the underpart is pale blue whilst over all there are silvery dots. The iris of the eyes and the fins are bright scarlet. The length may be up to four feet with the depth but little less and the weight a hundredweight or more. The mouth is protractile.

Specimens have been taken off Cornwall, Kent, several parts of the east coast, North Wales and Scotland. Occasionally a choice specimen will be exhibited in the higher-class fishmonger's in London and elsewhere, just as sturgeon are. Like that fish, they make very good eating indeed. The Norwegians call it 'the large salmon,' possibly because of the quality of the flesh.

THE JOHN DORY   *ZEIDAE*

The John Dory, *Zeus faber* (Plate 27), is our only common member of this curious family. It is an interesting fish and a most odd-looking one. The length may be twenty inches or more, but although the body is very deep it is very narrow. A seventeen-inch-long specimen, caught near the Nore, with a depth of seven inches exclusive of the fins weighed only two and three-quarter pounds. On the other hand, there is a record of a specimen of twenty-two and a half inches which weighed eighteen pounds.

The narrow shape is exploited by the dory in stalking the small fishes on which it feeds. Seeing it edge-on, these little fishes can little suspect that they are in the presence of an enemy. With a shimmying sort of movement it works nearer and nearer to its prey. Then, when within striking distance, its protrusible mouth shoots forward and engulfs the unsuspecting fish. That it has an enormous appetite there can be little doubt. From the stomach of a one-pound dory no fewer than eighteen sprats, two sand eels, a cuttlefish and several semi-digested, unidentifiable fishes were taken. A total length of nearly six feet of fish, and that from the stomach of a fish with a length of only fourteen and a half inches.

Another method used by the dory to catch its dinner, according to some observers, is to lie half buried in the sand with the shaggy filaments of the dorsal fin waving about in the water. Small fishes, attracted by this inviting bait, are soon dealt with.

The prevailing colour of the body is olive-brown suffused with a metallic sheen giving a blue, gold and yellow effect during life. On each side, just behind the pectoral fins, there is a circular black patch with a golden edging. This patch has given rise to the legend that this was the fish caught by St. Peter in the Sea of Galilee in the mouth of which was the tribute money. The mark was supposed to have been made by the Apostle's thumb when he held the fish to remove the money. It is more probable that the fish in question was a member of the Tilapia family, numbers of which abound in those waters.

Many people consider the dory to be one of the very choicest of food fishes and it is recorded that the eighteenth-century actor, James Quin, who was a gourmet of no mean standing, was very partial to a dish of dory. He thought nothing of journeying to Plymouth from Bath (to which latter place he had retired) just to have a dory straight from the sea and cooked in seawater.

Strangely enough, we know practically nothing of its breeding habits. We are not even certain of its breeding season, but Dr. James Murie was of the opinion that it had a winter or spring rather than summer or autumn spawning, from the condition of a female captured in November with ovaries fairly well developed. Recent observations indicate that it spawns in the summer.

THE BOAR-FISH   *CAPROIDAE*

The Boar-fish, *Capros aper* (Plate 27). At times this odd-looking, gaudy-red fish is very common off the Cornish coast and at scattered intervals specimens have wandered as far as Kent and the coast of North Wales. Sometimes, so the Channel fishermen declare, it becomes a nuisance by filling up their nets to the exclusion of other more profitable fishes. This has always struck me as being rather absurd for it is a splendid food fish itself, for all its small size, with white flesh of a flavour entirely its own.

The fins, with which it produces a curious stridulating sound, are of a rich, red colour and

across the base of the tail there is a dark band.
The eye is large and the sides of the body have a
rough feel due to small spines on the scales.

It is a bottom-loving fish and, as it has the same
narrow shape and protrusible mouth, probably
uses the same stalking technique as does the dory.
The length rarely exceeds six inches with a depth
of four inches. The spawning time is from June
to August. The eggs are pelagic and transparent with one oil-globule often of a yellow
colour.

THE SEA BASSES   *SERRANIDAE*

The Sea Basses are widely distributed throughout the temperate and, particularly, the tropic seas
of the world. Although some travel up-river a
considerable distance and stay in fresh water for
long periods, all spawn in the sea.

Four species have been recorded from British
waters, but only one of them is common. This is
the Common Bass, *Morone labrax* (Plate 30), one
of the most popular of fishes with the angler,
especially in southern waters. The other three
are the Stone Basse (the final ' e ' is not a misprint),
Polyprion americanus, the Dusky Perch, *Epinephelus gigas*, and the Comber, *Serranus cabrilla*.
Very few specimens have been found so there is
little point in dilating on them here.

The Bass is a handsome fish, of powerful build
and silvery colouring. The weight may be over
twenty pounds. It comes inshore to breed in
June—a month earlier on the west coast—and is
not averse to the brackish water of estuaries. In
these respects it resembles the mullet and the two

species are often found in each other's company. A seventeenth-century writer has succinctly remarked of them—'sucking mullet, swallowing bass'; an apt way of describing their feeding habits.

They live chiefly on fish and crustaceans, gobies, young eel-pout and the like, and rag, lug and other marine worms.

In the English Channel and, in particular, off the south coast of Ireland this fish is plentiful, but although it does not travel very far up the North Sea, angling for it from the pier at Walton-on-the-Naze and the beach at Frinton-on-Sea is a pastime that attracts enthusiasts from quite distant parts of the country.

As regards its breeding habits, it would seem that the adults travel from the deeper water in early summer with some of them branching westwards to Ireland and the others travelling up the English Channel. The eggs are more or less buoyant, just floating in sea water and not quite sinking to the bottom where the water is brackish to fresh. They are comparatively small—the diameter is between 1.15 mm. and 1.20 mm.—and the fry hatch out in six days, growing rapidly until between two and four inches in length. Growth eases up at the onset of winter when, presumably, the young fish have difficulty in finding suitable food.

Contrary to the generally accepted view, many of the young bass remain in certain areas, notably the Thames estuary, until February. The sprat-ters and shrimpers frequently find the little ones in their catch throughout the winter months. The possibility is that inshore trawlermen in other parts also find them but assume that they are the young of other fishes.

They may be identified, even in the inch-long stage, by the small scales, the nine spines in front of the dorsal fin, the three spines of the anal fin, the serrations of the pre-operculum and the spines on the operculum.

THE HORSE MACKERELS *CARANGIDAE*

Here again we encounter a family with three representatives in British waters but with only one of them at all common. They are the Pilot Fish, *Naucrates ductor*, the Glaucus, *Trachinotus glaucus*, and the Horse Mackerel, *Trachurus trachurus* (Plate 29).

The Pilot Fish travels the oceans of the Northern Hemisphere from the tropical to the temperate parts of the Atlantic, generally following or attendant upon a shark or a ship. That is how this pelagic fish from the open seas comes to visit our shores on occasion, and here again it is the milder south-western parts of the British Isles which are so honoured. There are seventeen or so records from Cornwall and they are also said to have been hooked at Dover.

The Glaucus, so-called from its green colour, is also a fish of the warmer Atlantic waters and the Mediterranean. There are only two British records, from places as far apart as the Isle of Skye and Marazion in Cornwall, both places coming within the influence of the Gulf Stream.

The Horse Mackerel, known also as the Scad, not to be confused with the Shad, *Alosa alosa*, is common in almost all temperate seas and is one of the most easily recognized of our fishes. This is by virtue of the row of large, plate-like scales or scutes which extend along the whole length of the lateral line, with a characteristic dip commencing between the first and second dorsal fins. The shape is definitely that of the mackerel yet the two fishes, although both in the same order, are not of the same family. The dorsal fins of the two fishes are dissimilar. There are two sharp spines just in front of the ventral fin as the unwary may find to their cost.

The angler may catch them by the same methods and bait as those used for the mackerel and although one rarely sees them offered for sale in the shops, except in parts of Cornwall, perhaps, they provide good eating, the taste being reminiscent of the common mackerel. Incidentally, the 'horse' part of the name is to do with the alleged coarseness of the flesh.

The so-called 'mackerel midge,' the tiny fishes which swarm near the surface at times, are related to neither fish, being the young stage of one of the Rocklings. They are greatly sought after by bass and mackerel.

Like the bass, the horse mackerel comes into our waters to spawn in early summer from the Atlantic. There seem to be two spawning areas, one at the westward entrance to the English Channel and the other off the Suffolk-Essex coast. The latter assumption is supported by the fact that, although the adults are rarely seen in the Thames estuary, immature and very young specimens are commonly found in the summer months and even into the winter, when the length will be about four inches.

The eggs float and are of a reddish appearance owing to the colouration of the oil globule. The young come inshore, and there are times when great numbers are found washed up on the beaches of Devon and Cornwall. At times solitary specimens will spend their time grubbing about on the seabed, but when they decide to go in shoals in search of pastures new they swim almost on the surface. This practice leads to the stranding on the beaches already referred to.

Its range in our part of the world is a wide one, some shoals venturing as far to the north as Trondhjem on the one hand, to Solway on the other. The favourite food appears to be the fry of the herring and pilchard and this would seem to be the reason for the choice of breeding ground.

THE 'DOLPHIN' BREAMS   *BRAMIDAE*

The true dolphin is a mammal and a relation of the whale and porpoise. The members of the fish family Coryphaenoididae, in which these particular breams were included, are also called, erroneously, dolphins. They are noted for their unusual shape, the small mouth with powerful, conical teeth and the colouring which, in some species, is particularly brilliant. This colouring turns to a leaden hue as soon as they die.

The Long-finned Bream, *Brama longipinnis*, is widely distributed—from Madeira to Iceland—but it is only common in the warmer seas and has only been recorded from Ireland, just the one specimen from Valencia Island in the extreme south-west of County Kerry.

Ray's Bream, otherwise the Black Sea Bream, *Brama raii*, is the species more commonly found off our coast. It is a deep-sea fish with a wide distribution; the whole length of the Atlantic except for the cold parts are its realm. Until recent years most of the records were of specimens found washed up on the shore. One such, found on the Northumberland coast in September 1868, weighed four and a half pounds and had a length of sixteen and three-quarter inches with a depth of eight and a half inches.

The colour is a deep olive brownish red along the dorsal and ventral surfaces and the whole is suffused with silver. The scales, though not large, are distinctive and overlap each other, in the words of Frank Buckland, like the scales on the shoulder straps of a Life Guard's cuirass. The whole of the head, too, is covered with scales in the same manner.

It is said to spawn south of the equator from whence, one would suppose, it travels northward into the Mediterranean and round the coast of Ireland and then on to Norway, etc. Strangely enough there do not seem to be any records of its being found south of Cromer although there is an annual migration to the Firth of Forth.

THE MEAGRES   *SCIAENIDAE*

The members of this family mostly inhabit the tropics and nearly all cover a wide range but none are of a more wandering disposition than the Meagre, or Maigre, *Sciaena aquila*. It is found off the coast of South Australia, in the Red Sea, off South Africa and the West Indies, and at least one or two specimens are caught every year from our waters, some having been recorded from Sussex and the outer part of the Thames estuary.

The length may be up to six feet and the weigh

seventy pounds or more. The colour is a rich yellowish bronze with a golden sheen overall, the head being silvery and the fins various shades of red. In the head are two beautifully designed ear bones and these the ancients used to grind to a powder and use as a cure for colic.

One of its common names is the Shade Fish; its generic name is derived from 'skia,' a ghost or shadow, and is probably earned from its habit of gliding gracefully amongst the great seaweeds. The Sea Sheep is another name by which it is known and this is due to the strange noise it makes in the water.

THE RED MULLETS *MULLIDAE*

There are more than fifty members of this family scattered over the oceans of the temperate and tropical parts of the world, only two species, however, being found in British waters. They are the Red Mullet, *Mullus surmuletus* (Plate 32) and the Striped Mullet, *Mullus barbatus*. For years controversy raged over these two species. Some authorities insisted that they were varieties of the one species and others that they were of totally different species. Raffaele, the Italian naturalist, who studied them in captivity in the Naples aquarium, stated that there is a difference in the diameter of the eggs, those of the Striped Mullet being larger than those of the Red Mullet.

The difference in the appearance of the adults is that the Red Mullet is uniformly red on the back and sides whilst the other has from three to five yellow bands passing from the head to the tail.

Although the habitat is from the Canaries to

Norway it is rarely taken in any numbers off the British coast except off Cornwall where the fry of about three inches in length are at times caught in great numbers. Curiously enough, the yolk sac of the larva is situated in the front part of the head region and not behind it as in most other fishes. As soon as the weather turns cool in autumn the mullets leave our shores for warmer climes.

Today, as in the times of the gluttonous Romans, this fish is greatly esteemed for the table and justly so. But I very much doubt whether one would feel inclined to pay £50 for one fish, yet that is just what the Emperor Claudius did. Quite a price for a fish which rarely exceeds three pounds in weight. The food consists of shrimps principally, with molluscs and worms as second choice.

THE SEA BREAMS   *SPARIDAE*

Although only one member of this family is common to the British Isles mention must be made also of the eight other Sea Breams which on infrequent occasions come to our shores. Some are less rare than others, but I am convinced that many more visit us than have been recorded.

They do not attain any great size—about twenty inches in length—but they are extensively fished for, especially in the tropical and temperate seas in which they abound. The shape and finnage greatly resemble the freshwater perch but, apart from the rather spectacular colouring, it is for the unusual teeth that they are mostly of interest.

These are a perfect crushing mill, so it is not surprising that the principal diet is of molluscs, even those with hard shells such as the whelk.

Also, they are so designed that they can deal adequately with limpets and other rock-loving molluscs.

Our most common and important species is the Common Sea Bream, *Pagellus centrodontus* (Plate 30), which is caught in what might be referred to as 'commercial quantities' off the south coast of England and Ireland. Unfortunately, as they have to be eaten as soon after capture as possible they are not a good market fish, other than at the port where they are landed.

The angler plying his art for conger off the Cornish coast at night might land a bream or two, especially in deepish water with a rocky bed. He can try for them at any depth, from the surface to the bottom, with mussels, the soft part of limpets, worms, squid or sand eel.

At times the young fish of about four inches or so in length (called locally 'chad') swarm inshore when they can be caught on small hooks without even using bait. They form good bait for other fishes.

The colour of the adult is orange-scarlet above with silvery sides. This is another of those fishes with a black spot on the shoulder, just behind the upper part of the gill-cover.

So far as is known the eggs of this fish are demersal whilst those of the other members of the family are pelagic, with the exception, perhaps, of *S. cantharus*.

Also found off the Cornish coast though by no means so frequently is the Old Wife or Black Seabream, *Spondyliosoma cantharus*. It also wanders as far north as the Tyne. The Gilthead, *Sparus aurata*, is more commonly found, not only along the southern coasts but also along the east coast as far as Scotland. It is a handsome fish, specimens from the Mediterannean may weigh up to sixty pounds, and well deserves its name of Gilthead. The head is an iridescent green with a golden band over the eyes.

The Spanish Sea Bream, otherwise known as Pandora or King of the Breams, *Pagellus erythrinus*, is not rare on the south coast and in the North Sea. Ordinarily it lives in the surf amongst the rocks searching out the molluscs and other titbits. Some say that it is not averse to an occasional meal of seaweed which it tears from the rocks with its powerful teeth. There is also the possibility that it is partial to the living coral found off the Cape of Good Hope.

Possibly even less frequently found is the Spanish Bream, *Pagellus bogaroveo*, which also wanders up and down the North Sea and off the south coast in the waters of the Atlantic.

The species of which only one or two or at most half a dozen individuals have ever been recorded from the British Isles are Dentex, *Dentex dentex*, which has been found off the south coast and Wales, the Bogue, *Box boops*, Couch's Sea Bream, *Pagrus pagrus*, the Axillary Bream, *Pagellus owenii*, and *Pagellus acarne*.

THE WRASSES   *LABRIDAE*

The wrasses are amongst the most beautifully coloured fishes in our fauna. They are also amongst the most economically useless. It is true that they are edible but for some reason or other their flavour is affected by whatever their diet happens to be at the moment, even to the point of being poisonous. This occurs, as with the parrot fishes, especially in tropic seas when they have been feeding on coral.

An interesting feature of the wrasse is its rate of breathing, which is remarkably slow. This has been estimated as being from twelve to eighteen respirations per minute, this also being the breathing rate of the Australian lung fish on a cool day. It steps up to thirty-one respirations per minute on a hot one. The little minnows and sticklebacks puff away at the rate of one hundred and fifty per minute.

Another interesting point about these beautiful fishes is the deliberate way they go to sleep at night. If a light is flashed into the aquarium in which they are housed they will be seen to be on the bottom, not resting on their undersides as do other fishes which sleep at night, but actually lying on their side. A most curious sight indeed.

Seven species are found around our coast wherever there are weed-covered rocks. Not, of course, that they are all commonly found, for some are very rare indeed. Still, many a youthful angler has a soft spot for these fishes for they probably formed his very first 'bag' as a sea angler. They can be angled for from the safe sort of rocky ledge, jutting slightly over the water, on which the watchful guardian will not be averse to sitting.

The food is of the same nature as that of the breams, that is to say, the molluscs, such as winkles, the small crustaceans and the worms which inhabit the seaweeds festooning out from the rocks. Consequently, the lips are thick and protrusible so as to cope with the nature of the fish's diet and habitat. For this reason, the Germans call the wrasses, as a whole, *Lippenfische*.

Although, as I have said, they are fishes of our rocky coasts generally, they grow to their largest and most colourful off our south-western shores. In the marine aquarium at Fowey in Cornwall there are always on exhibit huge, gorgeously coloured specimens of the Ballan, Cuckoo and other wrasses. Here one can see the amazing differences in the colouring of the different members of the same species.

The local names given to them are almost as varied as their garb. Thus, our most common species the Ballan Wrasse, *Labrus bergylta* (Plate 36), is also known as the Bergylt, Bergle, Sweet Lips, Sea Swine, Oldewe and Ancient Wife. The two last names arise, doubtless, from the Welsh name for this fish—*gwrach*, which means 'old woman.'

Generally, the colour of the Ballan is blue or green along the sides with orange, orange-red or yellow rings on the fins and sometimes on the body. The eggs are laid from May to July in a specially prepared nest loosely constructed of sea-weed. Some fishes lend themselves more readily to certain aspects of marine research and in this species the annual growth rings on the scales are very clearly marked (in some species they are most indistinct) and, as they are ideal aquarium fishes, the 'growth ring' theory can be proved with little difficulty.

The Cuckoo Wrasse, sometimes called the Red or Striped Wrasse, *Labrus mixtus* (Plate 33), is probably as common in British waters as the foregoing. It, too, has great colour variation not only between individuals but between the two sexes as well. In the male, on a background of varying shades of orange-red and yellow there are also blue bands, five or six in number, radiating backwards from the eye. In the female these bands are absent. The breeding habits are similar to those of the Ballan Wrasse. The two species may attain a length of eighteen inches.

Another common wrasse which also prefers southern waters is the Corkwing or Sea Partridge, *Crenilabrus melops* (Plate 36), sometimes known as the Gilt Head, a name which is apt to confuse it with the bream of that name. A feature which distinguishes it from the other Wrasses are the serrations on the edge of the pre-operculum. The colouring, too, is sufficient to set it apart from the others. The body part is green above, fading to a more silvery colour on the ventral surface with overall orange and yellow. From the dorsal fins about eight brown bar-like patches spread downwards to the lateral line. At the base of the tail there is also a brown patch. The eggs are laid loosely in a seaweed nest but they are not adhesive as are those of the two other nest makers.

The Gold-sinny or Gold-finney, *Ctenolabrus rupestris*, is also a southern species but it has been recorded from the Mersey estuary by Dr. Travis Jenkins. A wrasse which might well have been of this species was captured in a shrimp trawl in the Thames estuary in early April 1900. It was eight inches in length with a depth of three and a half inches, excluding the fins, and was a female with ovary about two-thirds ripe. The eggs are pelagic and the period of incubation is the shortest for any pelagic egg, two days.

This is perhaps the most satisfactory of all marine fishes to keep in the home aquarium. The size is comparatively small and the colours— golden-pink fading towards the abdomen with red fins—are always a delight. Moreover it is a lively fish and gets up to all sorts of antics in searching out the minute organisms on which it feeds from amongst the mass of seaweeds which should be replenished in the aquarium about every week. It is an inshore species.

The three remaining British wrasses are the Scale-rayed Wrasse, *Acantholabrus palloni*, the Rock Cook, *Centrolabrus exoletus*, and finally a species which is less rare than was formerly thought—the Rainbow Wrasse, *Coris julis* (Plate 33)—a fish of striking colouration due, principally, to the pale yellow indented band running from the operculum to the tail.

THE SAND EELS   *AMMODYTIDAE*

These are not eels, of course, but they look remarkably like them. Attenuated and silvery and with long, narrow dorsal fins their movement in the water is eel-like, too.

Until quite recent years it was thought that only two species of sand eel inhabited the coasts of the British Isles and many people were not convinced that these two species were distinct, so much are they alike. Now is has been discovered that large shoals of two other species wander into our waters.

The two commoner species are the Lesser Sand Eel, *Ammodytes tobianus* (Plate 31), and the Greater Sand Eel, *A. lanceolatus* (Plate 31). They may be distinguished by the greater projection of the lower jaw in the Greater and the presence of two strong teeth on the vomer, a bony plate in the roof of the mouth. Also the front end of the dorsal fin commences behind the pectoral fin. In the Lesser there are no teeth on the vomer and the dorsal fin commences immediately above the pectoral fin.

The habits of the two species are very similar. Both burrow in the sand, a feat that is assisted, or rather, made possible, by the horny, scoop-like lower jaw. With the aid of this they scoop their way at great speed into the wet sand of the sea-shore where they can remain for some time. The reason for this digging habit is, doubtless, to escape from their enemies. It is also possible that the small worms and crustacea which inhabit wet sand are an attraction.

In some places, when it is known that a shoal of these eels has 'gone to earth,' the local people will sally forth with spades to dig them out for they are only buried a few inches under the sand. There are two reasons for this hunting of the sand eel: they make excellent bait for bass, pollack and coal-fish and for some of the flat fishes as well, and they also make very good eating. In fact, in some parts the whitebait consists of young sand eels.

Their main diet consists of small sprats and the young of their own kind as well as crustaceans, especially young shore crabs.

The Lesser Sand Eel attains a length of seven inches and is abundant on almost all the shores of the British Isles, moving about in great shoals, especially in sandy estuaries. The eggs are laid at dead low water mark so that they are uncovered for only a little while and that only during spring tides. They are slightly adhesive and so they stick to the grains of sand which they very much resemble and this must help to protect them from creatures which like fish eggs. The eggs hatch out in ten days and the larvae are disconcertingly like the larvae of the herring. There is one great difference, however; the gut of the sand eel extends for the greater part of the fish's length, whereas that of the herring is short.

The Greater Sand Eel is a common enough fish but is not so abundant as its smaller relative. Also, it runs to a greater length and specimens of eighteen inches in length have been recorded, although twelve inches seems to be the more usual length. Its habits are similar, and so too are the breeding methods, but with this difference—the Lesser would appear to have two spawning periods, June and December, whilst the Greater has one extended period, from May to August.

The two other species are *A. cicerellus* and *A. marinus*, both of which have been found in deep water off the extreme north of Scotland.

THE WEEVERS   *TRACHINIDAE*

The two species of Weever Fish in our fauna are amongst the very few British fishes capable of inflicting a poisonous wound, a wound sufficiently venomous to cause great pain and, in certain circumstances, real illness to human beings, old and young alike.

By far the more common and also the more venomous species is the Lesser Weever, *Trachinus vipera* (Plate 31), which ranges all round our coasts, especially where the shallow, sandy seabed is conducive to the breeding of shrimps. Its habit is to lie half buried in the sand from which vantage point it can snap at the shrimps as they scuttle by. As a result the unwary visitor to the seaside who indulges in a paddle might quite easily tread on the upthrust spines and so receive a nasty shot of poison.

The poison is contained in a sac at the base of the spines of the first dorsal fin and of a spine projecting backwards from the operculum. These spines are grooved and, as a result, the poison shoots up them when they are pressed on to the sac. The poison fangs of snakes function in a similar manner. No one seems to know just why this particular genus should be so armed for it is no more vulnerable to attack from large fishes than any other small fish of the shallows. There is one point, incidentally, about the poison glands that I have noticed—after a specimen has been preserved in formalin for a little time a black patch forms at the base of the operative spines both of the dorsal fin and the operculum.

The principal victims of the weever's sting are the shrimpers, for mixed up in the heterogeneous material which the trawl brings up from the seabed frequently there are weevers. The process of 'culling' the catch consists first of throwing overboard all the unwanted stuff such as seaweeds, crabs, small fishes, jellyfishes, starfishes, etc., and putting aside the larger fishes and crabs and lobsters of marketable size. Under the best of conditions, when hands are thrust into the mass on the deck, it is difficult to avoid the weever, but on a dark, blowy morning it is impossible to see if the little fish you are grabbing is a weever.

The resultant wound is intensely painful and its effects may last for several days. Sometimes the joints of the fingers become permanently stiffened.

It is a greyish-coloured fish with a length of about six inches. The breeding season is from May to September.

The Greater Weever, *Trachinus draco* (Plate 32), is yellowish in colour rather than grey. The body is deeper than that of the other species and there are oblique bands on the sides. The eggs are laid some distance off shore in the North Sea from June to August and they are distinguishable from those of the Lesser by their smaller size and the presence of a single, large oil globule. In the Lesser there are several, small oil globules.

The length usually is about twelve inches (it seems to be the smaller specimens of the Greater Weever which come inshore) but there is a record of one being landed at Plymouth which had a length of seventeen and a half inches.

The strange thing about these two fishes is that the flesh is perfectly wholesome to eat and in some parts of the country they are offered for sale.

THE MACKERELS *SCOMBRIDAE*

The mackerels (Plate 13) are at once amongst the most colourful of fishes and the most powerful and graceful of swimmers. Some are of quite large size and all are excellent for the table, provided they are cooked as soon after capture as possible. This fish does not stay fresh for the same length of time as most other fishes; this probably is due to the fact that its muscles are more liberally supplied with blood vessels and nerves and also that its temperature, due to its excessive activity, is a few degrees above that of any other fish.

The Mackerel, *Scomber scombrus*, is said to be the only fish permitted to be offered for sale on Sundays because in the days before refrigeration those caught on Saturdays would not keep in hot weather until the Monday. True it is that the Sunday-morning mackerel seller, even today, is a feature of the landscape of many small seaside places.

To the sea angler the mackerel is a godsend, for its fairly long season is at the best time of the year for angling (spring to autumn) and the angling for it embraces numerous techniques.

The food consists of small planktonic crustaceans which it sieves from the water with its gill-rakers, this generally in the earlier part of the year, and of sprats, small pilchards and other similar fishes. At times it will seek the sea bed in search, presumably, of worms and small, bottom-loving fishes.

The habitat is a curiously restricted one, in a way, for although it is a powerful swimmer and covers great distances in its travels and is often in vast shoals it is rare along the east coast from about the Wash northwards and also is less common on the north-east coast of Ireland. Yet the Isle of Man has an extensive fishery which lasts from May to September. It may prefer the warmer currents.

The shoals approach our shores from the Atlantic fairly early in the year, although in March and April they are still twenty to thirty miles from the land where the main spawning grounds are. In May, when some shoals are still spawning, they come closer inshore where they remain until about the end of September before they drift off into deep water again. In some places, however, they have been taken at all times of the year. This is particularly so at Plymouth.

They are one of the most easily recognized of fishes with their powerful, torpedo-shaped body and the unusual finlets behind the second dorsal fin and also behind the ventral fin. The colour, too, is striking, especially on being landed. Black wavy bands pass down to the mid-dorsal line and between them the colour is deep green. The sides and underside are iridescent and silvery. At the anterior and posterior ends of the eyes there are transparent lids which, at times, give them a semi-blind appearance. The length of this fish may be up to eighteen inches and the weight up to two and a half pounds.

The female, in early summer, lays up to half a million eggs and these, too, are of migratory habits. First of all, for about two days, they float on the surface, then they sink to midwater where they remain for a few days and eventually they sink to the bottom. The young mackerel of about three inches in length swarm in both the English and Bristol Channels. In fact the Normandy fishermen catch them with seine nets and they are then canned in the same way as sardines.

The Spanish Mackerel, *Pneumatophorus colias*, as the name suggests is a native of the Bay of Biscay and the other warmer parts of the Atlantic. It is a powerful swimmer and somewhat of a wanderer and, as a result, occasional specimens visit Britain mostly in the water off the south-west peninsula. The shape is very much like that of the Common Mackerel but they may be distinguished by the corselet of largish scales below the pectoral fin and the larger eyes of the Spanish Mackerel. This fish also possesses an air-bladder which is absent in the common species.

The most spectacular of the mackerel family is the Tunny fish, a fish of the Mediterranean of great size which, in its home waters, may attain a weight of over a thousand pounds. Not so very many years ago they were considered as being extremely rare in British waters but now, during the season, what might be described as deep-sea anglers land a fair number of them, especially when a shoal decides to invade the North Sea. When this happens the news soon gets about and from Scarborough and other angling resorts the angler goes out after them.

The equipment is costly, for the rod is a special steel one and the winch differs considerably from those ordinarily used in fishing. Also, the angler has to wear a special kind of harness in which the butt of the rod rests. Moreover, a sturdy motor boat is required. All these things cost money. Still, they can be hired and some angling clubs possess their own equipment which is hired out to members at quite low cost. Specimens of over four hundred pounds are not infrequently brought into harbour, generally after the angler has tussled with his opponent for hours and aches from head to foot.

The species mostly caught is the Short-finned or Common Tunny, *Thunnus thynnus* (Plate 34), which, from time to time, at long intervals, takes a look into the Thames estuary. As with most of the warmer Atlantic fishes, the south-west coast receives the greater number of visits and from thence it migrates round the west and north coasts into the North Sea.

Both this species and the Long-finned Tunny, also known as the Germon or Albacore, *Germo alalunga*, differ from the mackerel in the second dorsal fin being continuous with the first dorsal. Also there is a distinct corselet of scales starting large from the pectoral fin and becoming smaller towards the tail. In the Long-finned species this corselet is rather obscure, but the pectoral fin is much longer, about one-third of the length of the body, and is sickle-shaped. It is also a much smaller fish although in its native Mediterranean it may have a length of five feet and weigh about one hundred pounds. There are records of its capture off Cornwall, Scotland and Ireland.

Others members of the family with several British records to their credit are the Pelamid, *Sarda sarda*, also known as the Belted Bonito, which has a smaller corselet and broad bands passing down from the back and narrow bands slanting across them downwards and forwards, and the Bonito or Stripe-bellied Tunny, *Katsuwonus pelamis*. These are much smaller fishes than the two principal species of tunny, having a length of about two feet and a weight of ten pounds. The Bonito is also a fish with striking markings. In this species there are four or five long, curved blue bands passing along the sides and belly and curving upwards to end on the lateral line or just above it.

The Plain Bonito, *Auxis rochei*, has only been recorded from Cornwall. It is somewhat larger than the mackerel and can be distinguished from it by the corselet on the breast region and from the Tunny and the two foregoing by the two dorsal fins being separate.

THE SWORD FISHES   *XIPHIIDAE*

These are the largest and most powerful of all the true fishes and the most difficult to study. This is for two reasons: the difficulty of capturing this powerful and dangerous fighter which has led to there being only a few specimens in the world's museums; and the curious changes an individual will undergo from one part of its life to another. Its fry were known years before it was realized that they were sword-fish fry.

They are also probably the fastest swimming fishes in the sea and when this is taken into account with their size (up to fifteen feet) and weight (up to a ton) it is little wonder that they can pierce the planks of ships.

No one has been able to account satisfactorily for their habit of repeatedly stabbing whales with the 'sword,' a prolongation of the upper maxillary and intermaxillary bones, for they do not collect any food that way. Possibly they do it in order to get their blow in first; possibly they move so fast through the water that they cannot put the brakes on in time. At any rate, one specimen nine feet in length and weighing two and a half hundred-weights charged head first into a mudbank in the River Roach near Foulness Island, Essex, in 1862, and was thus captured alive by some fishermen. Was this an accident or did it mistake the sandbank for a whale. Who knows?

Anyway, this amazing fish is by no means so rare on the British coast as might be thought. It has been recorded from most areas, generally in the late summer and autumn. It spawns in the Mediterranean in spring and early summer.

THE GOBIES   *GOBIIDAE*

These little fishes are amongst the most attractive of all our native fishes. They inhabit, according to the species, every part of our coast and are easily observable either in rock pools or runnels and guts on the sands. The colouring, too, is not only interesting, it is also, in its own way, quite beautiful. With the little crabs gobies are the scavengers of the littoral areas, especially in estuaries and creeks where they abound in myriads.

A close examination of the colouring, irrespective of species, shows that the surface of the body is more or less freckled, the freckles being of various separate colours. In some species they form distinct patterns. This form of colouring gives to the goby chameleon-like qualities. Thus, when the Freckled Goby, for example, is basking in the sun in a shallow runnel in the sand it is quite invisible. Its presence is only noticeable when it moves and this is frequently for it is a restless little fellow. In moving it makes a slight disturbance in the sand like a tiny cloud and this, and its shadow when it leaves the bottom, reveals its whereabouts.

The disturbance in the sand is brought about by the curious form of the pectoral fins. They meet on the underside of the fish and at their junction is a shallow, cup-like sucker formed actually by the bases of the fins themselves, the body part not entering into it at all. With this sucker the gobies can adhere to rocks and even to the sand.

One of our gobies, the Diminutive Goby (Plate 40), has the distinction of being one of the smallest of fishes; the very smallest fish is also a goby, *Mistichthys luzonensis*, which is found only in one of the lakes in Luzon in the Philippines. Its total length when fully grown is only half an inch. It also has the honour of being the smallest of all known vertebrates. Strangely enough, although it is so diminutive it forms an important item of food because it is so remarkably prolific. Our gobies have no economic value save as forming the diet of many valuable food fishes.

The male changes his colour during the spawning season which starts in early spring. At mating time the procedure seems to consist of the male finding a suitable spot where the eggs will be laid and then going out to find a mate. The chosen spot might be a flat stone in some sheltered spot or an empty mussel, cockle or other shell, sometimes just a clump of seaweed. The eggs are oval in shape and are large. They are fastened at their base by an outspread network by which they are anchored to the 'nest.' From the time the female starts to deposit the eggs until they hatch out the male guards them valiantly, giving battle to any intruder. With his large pectoral fins he fans the water to provide a current of water over the eggs. In the meantime the female has gone off to find another mate. The father does not seek another mate until his offspring are all hatched out.

The shape of the gobies is basically the same for all species, a big head, large eyes placed right on top of the head and nearly touching, two dorsal fins often brightly marked, and rounded tail.

The gobies, by virtue partly of their protective colouration and partly because they are of insignificant size and of no commercial value, have never received any special attention from the ichthyologist. As a result, species which have hitherto been considered extremely rare are, in effect, not so much rare as localized.

Thus the Giant Goby, *Gobius capito*, which was not recognized as being a British species until 1903, has probably always been quite common in the Channel and in the rock pools between Fowey and Falmouth where, at times, a dozen or more may be seen in the one pool. It is by far our largest goby and attains a length of nine inches The smaller specimens could be confused with the Black Goby, *Gobius niger* (Plate 44) but there is one particular difference; in the first dorsal fin the mid-rays are the longest whereas in the Black Goby all the rays are of the same length.

The Black Goby is found all round the British coast. As the name suggests it is a dark coloured species of variable colouring with a distinct black effect generally. The length may be up to five inches.

The Rock Goby, *Gobius paganellus* (Plate 37), is a slightly smaller species than the foregoing; nevertheless, taken size for size all three might easily be mistaken one for the other. It is, however, more clearly marked especially on the first dorsal fin and it is never blackish in colour. The scales are smaller, too.

Fries' Goby, *Gobius friesii* (Plate 37), is essentially an Irish species and, apart from one recorded from Norway and two from Sweden, it has been found nowhere else. It has been found around most parts of the Irish coast where the bottom is of muddy sand. Identification of this species should not be difficult. On the head and gill covers there are conspicuous papillae and the rays of the first dorsal fin are produced into filaments. The caudal fin, too, is distinctive in being spear-shaped.

The Common Goby, *Gobius minutus*, appears to have two distinct forms, one which attains a maximum length of three and a half inches (the adult average is from two to three inches) and a smaller one with a maximum length of two and a half inches. The larger variety seems to prefer water with a normal salinity whereas the smaller one frequents the brackish water of creeks and salting pools and the inner part of estuaries. The colour is variable but three of the names it is commonly known by are quite apt: the Freckled, Yellow or One-spotted Goby. The last of these appellations refers to the deep-blue spot situated at the posterior end of the first dorsal fin. In rocky shores facing the open sea the colouring is at its brightest, whereas on muddy shores it is dingy. This is due, more than anything else, to the chameleon-like behaviour of the colour cells sprinkled over the body.

Not infrequently I have encountered them at banquets where they have gate-crashed into the whitebait. This is not surprising for they frequently accompany the shoals of baby herrings and sprats which compose the whitebait.

The Spotted Goby, *Gobius ruthensparri*, is found all round the British coast, especially in shallow, weedy water, and is very common in the Irish Sea. The 'spotted' part of the name is derived from the conspicuous black spot at the base of the tail. Other distinguishing features are the dark markings, five or six in number, which extend from the back to the lateral line and the red and yellow horizontal bands on the first dorsal fin. The length is two and a half inches.

Another well distributed species is the well-named Painted Goby, *Gobius pictus* (Plate 40), an inhabitant of areas where the seabed is of sand or sand and shingle and at a depth of up to fifteen fathoms. Like many other striking fishes, especially tropical aquarium fishes, a dingy body colour offsets brightly coloured fins. In this case both the spiny first dorsal and the second dorsal bear bands of colour, red on a pale background with black spots between the fin rays. Otherwise it is similar in size and shape to the smaller variety of the Common Goby.

Here again in the Diminutive or Scorpion Goby we have a species which is probably more frequent in our deeper waters than would appear from the scanty records of its capture. With a length of but one inch when fully grown it would escape through even the finest mesh permitted to be used in any form of trawling in Britain. True, in the pilchard haul specimens might well be trapped in the mass of fish in the cod end. But they would be discarded with the other 'rubbish.' It can be recognized by the broad, pale band across the base of the tail, the red horizontal bands on the second dorsal fin and the stout build.

In the Slender, White or Transparent Goby, *Aphya minuta*, we have another fish that is far more common than is generally thought. Its small size—a length of but one and a half inches—and its transparency have been responsible for its being so easily overlooked. Thus it was supposed to be rare off the coasts of Kent and Essex and in the Thames estuary, but Murie proved it to be particularly common, even as far up-river as Tilbury marshes and beyond.

The shape is a typical goby shape, also the pectoral fins form a disc and there are two dorsals, the first of which has fine spiny rays.

According to Professor R. Collet who in 1870-2 made a detailed study of this species in what was then Christiania Fiord the White Goby has a life span of only one year. Spawning took place, he wrote, in June, July and August; by the end of the autumn it had reached its full growth, and it died after spawning in the following summer. Murie, who made a study of these fishes in the Thames estuary, spread over thirty years, also found this to be the case, but he did not agree as to its living for only one year. His reasons for this he never published.

Another curious thing noted by Collet was that at breeding time the males lost the single row of small teeth, a characteristic of the species, and developed a single row of long teeth. In fact, so different does the male appear at breeding time that it was considered as being a different species.

THE DRAGONETS   *CALLIONYMIDAE*

On seeing one of the Dragonets for the first time one feels rather like the small boy and his first giraffe—you just do not believe it. Outlandish colours and odd-shaped fins and a strangely flatted head; that sums up the Dragonet. Indeed, one angler who brought me a specimen thought that he had caught a deformed fish and had decided that when it was young its head must have been trapped under a bar of metal or something and, in consequence, growth in the head had been arrested and so the fins had grown abnormally.

There are two British species, one being more colourful than the other but both are of bizarre design.

The Common Dragonet or Sculpin, *Callionymus lyra*, is by far the more common of the two species and is found in shallow waters all round the British Isles. It is not generally regarded as being a gregarious species yet at times, especially during the summer, they shoal in large numbers. This has been particularly noted in hauls from the Thames estuary, the Humber and the west coast of Ireland.

Courtship is rare amongst marine fishes yet this species is noted for the elaborate nuptial display it puts on. Moreover, the two sexes are strikingly different in appearance. The male is much larger—twelve inches in length compared with the total length of eight inches in the female—and much more colourful. In fact, so different do they appear that at one time they were thought to be two distinct species—the Gemmeous Dragonet and the Sordid or Dusky Dragonet.

The colour of the male is yellowish or orange and along each side of the body are two blue stripes with a row of light blue or greenish-blue spots above. The head bears violet-blue stripes and the fins are banded in yellow, green and blue. The fins of the male, are larger too, and the first dorsal has very long, flexible rays the front one of which extends backwards to the base of the caudal fin.

The female is a dull, yellowish brown paling into white on the underside and this is enlivened by numerous greenish spots ringed with brown.

The procedure at breeding time is for the male to rush around, driving away any other male and showing off for the benefit of the female. Then he swims round her displaying his fine fins and gorgeous colouring. When eventually he secures her affections he places his pelvic fin beneath hers and so virtually lifts her to the surface vertically, the eggs and the milt being deposited in the course of the journey. The eggs rise with them and at the surface the male and the female bid farewell to each other and leave the eggs unprotected.

The eggs are peculiar in possessing an outside network egg-membrane yet these reticulated processes have nothing to adhere to other than the surface of the water. This they do when the eggs are in a jar of water, but it is hardly feasible that they do so to the surface of the sea.

The Spotted Dragonet, *Callionymus maculatus* (Plate 41), has similar breeding habits to the foregoing. It is reputedly a much rarer species but it is reasonable to assume that, owing to the variations in the colouring, the females of the one might well be confused with those of the other.

The principal difference is in the colouration of the second dorsal fin on which there are distinct rows of spots. In the Common Dragonet they are either indistinct or missing altogether.

With both species the larvae spend their time on the surface and sink to the bottom in winter. The breeding season is a protracted one and lasts from April to September according to the locality.

THE BLENNIES *BLENNIIDAE*

Since the Cat-fish, *Anarhichas lupus* (Plate 44), has been transferred to another family there are now no blennies with any economic value whatever. Taking them by and large, with few exceptions, they are an uninteresting looking family but what they lose in glamour they make up for in other ways. They are a coastal fish with a preference for temperate or warm waters and they are not averse to brackish water.

The shape is very much like that of the goby, except that it is grosser and lacks the sprightliness of that little fish. The scales are either rudimentary or absent altogether and partly for that reason the fish have a slimy, slithery feel. In fact, one species is actually called the Butter-fish because of that.

The dorsal fin occupies almost the entire length of the back, even joining up with the caudal fin. In some species there is a partial break in the dorsal fin so that it is divided partially into two or three fins.

Blennies may be divided into three separate groups. Of those in which the dorsal fin is imperfectly divided into two and is separate from the caudal fin, the most common is the Common Blenny or Shanny, *Blennius pholis* (Plate 35), sometimes, because it has no scales, called the Smooth Blenny. In this species the division of the dorsal fin is only slight. The colour is a greenish ochre, blotched with dark spots. The fins are of a yellow colour, also with black spots. The outer edge of the anal fin has a black margin with a white outer rim. Although this is a common British species it certainly seems to prefer a shallow rocky situation for it is on rocky ledges that the eggs are laid; a habit which it also shares with the little *Copeina arnoldi*, a freshwater fish from Brazil. The male keeps guard on the eggs until they hatch out.

With a length of about nine inches the Gattorugine or Tompot, as it is called in Cornwall, *Blennius gattorugine*, is the largest of our blennies. It is a southern species and has rarely been found north of Kent or the Bristol Channel. It may readily be distinguished from the foregoing species by the fringed, fleshy tentacle above each eye.

The Butterfly Blenny (Plate 38) belongs to the same group as the two foregoing. It is commonly found in summer and autumn off the south-west coast. The most easterly limit seems to be Dover and its most northerly, Morecambe Bay, and then only rarely. This is a little fish with handsome finnage, the elevated dorsal fin having a striking black spot, fringed with white. This enhances the 'butterfly' effect.

The favourite habitat is rocky, weedy ground where the small crustaceans and other minute creatures on which the blennies feed abound. As with the Gattorugine there are tentacles arising from the skull between the eyes. The total length of the adult is seven inches. The breeding habits are similar to those of the Shanny.

Montagu's Blenny, *Blennius montagui* (Plate 35), may be recognized by the fold of skin between the eyes fringed with tiny tentacles. Also, the whole of the body and the fins, with the exception of the anal fin, carry numerous bluish-white spots whilst the body has, in addition, large, white patches. The dorsal fin is more clearly divided than in the two foregoing species. It is an inhabitant of the coastal waters of southern England and Ireland.

In August the female lays a carpet of eggs on the underside of stones and the male, in true blenny fashion, mounts guard over them. For the rest of the summer and autumn the fry inhabit the plankton, later to seek the less boisterous winter conditions amongst the rocks.

Yarrell's Blenny, *Chirolophis galerita* (Plate 35), is our only northern species in this family, having a range from Norway to the south coast. There are two pairs of tentacles on the head, the dorsal fin is continuous and undivided and it also has scales,

even though they are small ones. The breeding season is a very late one, October and November. The eggs sink to the bottom and when the fry hatch out they spend part of the winter with the plankton. The length may be up to seven and a half inches.

THE BUTTER-FISHES   *PHOLIDAE*

In this close relation of the blennies (Plate 45) the dorsal fin is not even slightly divided. Indeed, with the anal fin, it practically joins up with the tail fin. The body is long and slender and there is a striking row of white-fringed black spots along the base of the dorsal fin on each side. For this reason the Gunnel, *Pholis gunnellus*, is known to the east coast fisherman as 'nine eyes.' As with the closely related blennies, the Gunnel or Butter-fish has an amazing solicitude for its eggs.

The eggs are laid during the winter, from December to March, and for so small a fish—in the Thames estuary they run to about seven inches in length—these eggs are quite large, two milli-metres in length and just over a millimetre in diameter. When she lays them the female gathers them into a ball about the size of a golf ball, having first, if possible, found the shelter of some empty bivalve shell for protection.

Possibly the male and female take it in turn to be wrapped around the eggs, to afford them protection until they are hatched out a month after being laid. I rather feel that the male takes a hand in the matter, for one of its close relations from the Pacific has, on the male, a bony hook projecting from the front of the head and from this, on either side like the ears of a spaniel, hang two bunches of eggs.

The range and habitat of this species—the slipperiest of all the blenny kind—is similar to that of the foregoing species.

THE VIVIPAROUS BLENNIES
ZOARCIDAE

The Viviparous Blenny, *Zoarces viviparus* (Plate 38), has a long body tapering towards the tip of the tail with a curious notch in the edge of the dorsal fin towards the tail. The tail fin is not separate from the dorsal and anal fins. The scales are rudimentary and the fish has a very slimy, eel-like feel when handled. The length of the fully grown adult is up to twelve inches. The Eel Pout, as it is sometimes called, is common all round our coasts, especially near the mouths of rivers. Yarrel mentions them venturing as far up the River Thames as Greenwich.

They make wholesome eating, yet for the most part, no matter how large the catch, they are thrown back into the water along with the other 'rubbish' in the trawl. At one time, however, they were sold regularly in Edinburgh.

Towards winter time the larger specimens come inshore where they congregate until the spring and then they disperse, leaving behind the fry and other small ones. This fish is one of the very few which do not deposit eggs. Instead, the young are brought forth at a fairly advanced stage of development. This means that the eggs must be fertilized whilst still within the ovary of the female. As with the 'live-bearing' cyprinodonts of the tropics the male possesses an intromittent organ which in this case consists of an elongated papilla. Most fishes have paired ovaries but in *Zoarces* the roe is single and lies along the mid-line of the body. Twenty days after the spermatozoa has penetrated the micropyle of the egg the larvae emerge, but another three months is to elapse before they are 'born.'

They live partly on the yolk sac, as do the larvae of other fishes, and partly on the albuminous fluid secreted by the walls of the ovary. When they are discharged the length will be an inch and a half and when it is realized that a fully grown female may give birth to as many as three hundred at once some idea will be obtained of how neatly they are packed within the ovary—nearly forty feet of little fishes if put end to end.

The food consists of crustaceans and worms and, although of little or no economical importance themselves, they provide food for the more valuable food fishes.

THE SEA CAT-FISHES
ANARHICHADIDAE

These are by far the largest of the blenny allies and are represented in our fauna by the Wolf-fish or Cat-fish, *Anarhichas lupus*, and the more rare Lesser Cat-fish, *Anarhichas minor*.

The deeper parts of the North Sea and the sub-Arctic regions are their home and they are rarely found in water of less than thirty fathoms depth. The Lesser Cat-fish is commonly found round Iceland and is sometimes taken off the Shetlands. The two species differ in colouration. In the

Lesser the dark bands which are so characteristic of its larger relative are replaced by large black spots on the head, fins and body.

A. lupus attains a length of six feet and is of typical tabby cat colouration, being grey with the black transverse bands already mentioned. The dorsal fin extends unbroken from just behind the head to just in front of the tail. The anal fin extends for slightly more than half the entire length of the fish. The head is blunt and the jaws powerful, as well they need be to cope with the hard shells of the whelks, sea-urchins and large crustacea on which it feeds. The teeth, too, are of more than passing interest; in the front of each jaw there are a group of long, curved fangs, behind these there are rounded grinding teeth, two rows on the lower jaw on each side whilst on the roof of the mouth there are three rows, those on the outside being pointed and those in the centre being flat.

In one way or another it is a rather fearsome-looking creature and for this reason it is only rarely seen in its entirety on the fishmonger's slab. Instead, it is decapitated and skinned at the fishing port before being sent, as it is, to all parts of the country to be sold as 'rock salmon.' This euphemistic title is bestowed on any fish that, although being perfectly wholesome, would not appeal to the housewife in its natural state. Other fishes in this category are the Monk fish, *Squatina squatina*, and the Angler fish, *Lophius piscatorius*.

The eggs are exceptionally large, a quarter of an inch in diameter, and are deposited in December or January. They are adhesive and so they rest on the seabed in large, ball-like masses of yellowish colour. Whether the male protects the mass of eggs or not we do not know, but it is reasonable to assume from analogy that he does as in the case of the other blenny species. The larval cat-fish takes three and a half months to absorb the contents of its yolk-sac as compared with the week or two of most other marine fishes.

Although, as I have said, it is essentially a fish of northern waters there are isolated records of its capture in southerly regions. Thus, on 29 August 1885 one was captured at Walton-on-the-Naze and another, in 1938, at Battlesbridge, which is also in Essex. I only know about the 1938 specimen from a photograph taken by a local pressman; by the time I had located its captor he had disposed of it to numerous housewives in the district.

THE GREY MULLETS   *MUGILIDAE*

There seems to be some confusion and not a little dissension amongst the authorities as to how many British species of Grey Mullet there are and also as to the species themselves (Plate 48). The most general view is that the three British species are the Thick-lipped Grey Mullet, *Mugil chelo*, the Thin-lipped Grey Mullet, *Mugil capito*, and the Golden Grey Mullet, *Mugil auratus*. On one point, however, they are more or less unanimous and that is that the Thick-lipped species is by far the most commonly found in our waters. The remarks which here follow, then, are to do with that particular species.

It is a handsome fish, of elegant shape and of attractive, though subdued, colouring. The upper part, above where the lateral line would be if there was one, is an olive-green colour with the belly almost white. Overall it is silvery with narrow dark bands running horizontally along the back.

In summer, sometimes early, sometimes late, the fish move in from the sea to return in autumn. They venture into river estuaries and are not averse to the rather murky conditions found in harbours. There, doubtless, a favourite form of food has its habitation. They are a restless, unpredictable fish as the angler well knows and, from their peculiar method of feeding, an exasperating one. It does not tie up with any of the usual forms of angling.

The lips are leathery and the only form of dentition is a fringe of minute bristles. To observe the method of feeding and habits in general I find that the marshland creeks offer the best vantage points. Early on a summer morning with that faint haze which promises a hot day I settle myself on an old landing stage or decaying barge which is festooned with long strands of grass-like weed. The mullet can be seen coming into the creek with the incoming tide with the abandon of children being let out of school, sometimes, in their ebullience even leaping right out of the water. The whole shoal approaches the weed, hesitates and then makes a dart forward and a few moments later a dart back again. In that time each has grabbed a strand of weed with its mouth and sucked off it the tiny organisms attached to it, diatoms, minute crustaceans and molluscs and the like. The operation is repeated until the shoal is alarmed or the tide turns, then out to sea they go.

But principally the mullets feed by scraping the surface of the mud and extracting the decomposing vegetable matter and minute organisms found there. As a result the alimentary tract is a most unusual one. Pharyngeal bones separate the inorganic matter in the mud and this is then spat out. Due to this strange diet the stomach is thick-walled and muscular as is the stomach of the Irish Gillaroo Trout which feeds on molluscs. In the mullet it is much like the gizzard of a fowl. The intestine is connected with the assimilation of the food into the blood and in vegetarians and mud-eaters it has to be very long to provide the maximum of absorption surface. In a thirteen-inch mullet the intestine will be seven feet in length, consequently, in order to be housed, it has many folds and convolutions.

Purely carnivorous fishes have short guts only slightly convoluted.

Mullet are difficult to catch with rod and line, but some anglers are more successful than others and this, they claim, is due to their own particular type of paste. They are caught by means of seine nets but if only one of the shoal finds a loophole the whole catch will escape with it.

During the daytime they swim in shoals, either on the surface or browsing on the weeds. At night they settle to the bottom singly but at the slightest disturbance they will congregate immediately.

They attain a weight of four pounds or more and specimens with a length of three feet have been recorded.

THE SAND SMELTS   *ATHERINIDAE*

The Sand Smelts (Plate 39) are not to be confused with the true smelt. The former is readily recognizable by the absence of the cucumber scent, its short, bluntish head, large eyes, and bigger, rayed second dorsal fin. The true smelt is a Salmonoid and so has a small, adipose, dorsal fin. The Sand Smelt has a distinctive silver band along its sides.

It is a coastal fish, coming inshore for the summer and moving to deeper water for the winter. Spawning is in June and July. The eggs of the Atherine or Common Sand Smelt, *Atherina presbyter*, are demersal and, in common with many other demersal eggs, have filaments to enable them to adhere to some solid object on the seabed. The length of the adult does not exceed six inches; nevertheless on parts of the south coast they are considered a delicacy for the table, being cooked like sprats. In some places the fry are cooked as whitebait.

Although more a fish of the south coast they are also found in the North Sea as far as the Firth of Forth.

THE SEA PERCHES *SCORPAENIDAE*

The Sea Perch or Norway Haddock, *Sebastes marinus* (Plate 45), is more commonly referred to as the Bergylt by the fishmonger. It has a distinctly perch-like shape and this and its red colouring make it readily distinguishable from the other fishes on the slab. Only very rarely has it been taken from British waters; this is partly because it prefers water up to 150 fathoms in depth. But I have included it in this book because it is so frequently seen at the fishmonger's and our own trawlers bring large numbers into our northern fishing ports.

The Norwegian coast finds it at its most prolific and it is also taken between Iceland and the Shetlands.

This is one of the few viviparous marine bony fishes and it has been estimated that it may have as many as a thousand embryos in each ovary. The process of emptying the ovaries of the season's batch of eggs is a long one, lasting from April to July, because in a fully grown female there may be up to 148,000 eggs all waiting their turn to develop sufficiently to be born.

The average weight is about four pounds but they are said to attain a weight of twenty pounds.

THE GURNARDS   *TRIGLIDAE*

The head region of the gurnards (Plate 49) is strongly armoured with bony plates and has an angular appearance. It occupies quite a large part of the fish and the deepest part at that. They are spiny fishes, too, with large scales along the lateral line. Consequently, before being cooked they have to be beheaded and skinned and only a very small part of the original fish remains. For this reason and because of the trouble entailed it is not so widely sought after as it otherwise deserves to be, for it is as sweet a fish as ever came out of the sea.

We have six species, only three of which are common to our shores, the other three being chance visitors to the south-west coast.

The most common is the Grey Gurnard, *Trigla gurnardus* (Plate 49), and it is found all round our shores, particularly in the Irish Sea and off Scotland. In Scotland it is known as the

'Crooner' because of the crooning or groaning noise it makes when captured. This noise is made by special muscles lying in the walls of the swim bladder which, by vibrating rapidly when they are contracted, make the groaning noise.

Another striking feature of this and the other gurnards is the structure of the front rays of the pectoral fins. They are modified to form separate 'fingers,' three on each side. These serve several purposes, for disturbing sand or stones and exploring shells in the pursuit of food and also as a means of locomotion. The swimming part of the fish, in most species, is the latter half of the body with its terminating tail. In the gurnards the caudal fin is small and the adjacent part of the body too tapering to afford the necessary resistance to the water for powerful swimming. So these leg-like fingers are used as a form of locomotion also, but not, as one might think, for forward movement only, but also for backward movement.

This species is recognizable by the grey colour and its white spots. The scales along the lateral line, too, are noteworthy for the spines they bear.

The food consists of small crabs, sand eels and such molluscs as inhabit the seabed. Breeding time is from April to August when the orange-coloured pelagic eggs are laid. The mature male will have a length of seven inches and the female a length of just over nine inches. The species is also known as Bloch's Gurnard, a delicate compliment to Mark Eliezer Bloch, born in 1723, later a physician in Berlin and one of the very greatest of all students of fish life.

The Tub-fish, *Trigla lucerna* (Plate 42), has quite a number of common names and may be called the Sapphirine, Yellow, Swallow or Latchet

Sea Lamprey (p. 39)
Lampern (p. 39)
Eel (p. 65)

Pl. 1

Basking Shark (p. 45)
Thresher Shark (p. 44)

Pl. 2

Blue Shark (p. 48)
Smooth Hound (p. 49)

Pl. 3

Pl. 4

Porbeagle (p. 42)
Tope (p. 48)

Lesser Spotted Dogfish (p. 46)
Larger Spotted Dogfish (p. 47)
Piked Dogfish (p. 50)

Pl. 5

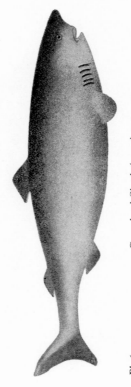

Greenland Shark (p. 50)

Pl. 6

Monk Fish (p. 51)

Pl. 7

Pl. 8   Common Skate (p. 53)

Pl. 9   Thornback Ray (male) (p. 55)

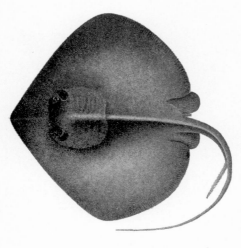

Pl. 10   Sting Ray (p. 56)

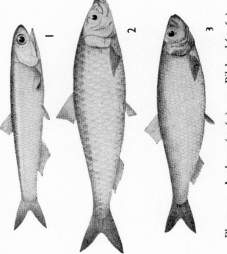

Pl. 11   1. Anchovy (p. 62).   2. Pilchard (p. 61).
3. Sprat (p. 60)

Pl. 12

Sturgeon (p. 58)
Allis Shad (p. 61)

Herring (p. 59)
Mackerel (p. 103)

Pl. 13

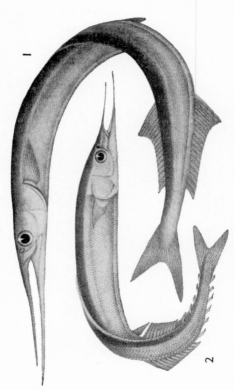

Pl. 14   1. Garfish (p. 68)   2. Saury Pike (p. 67)

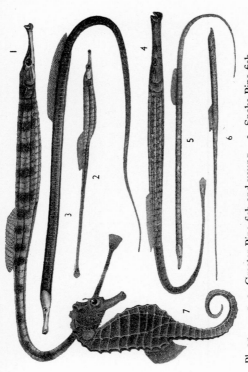

Pl. 15   1, 2. Greater Pipe-fish and young. 3. Snake Pipe-fish.
4. Broad-nosed Pipe-fish. 5. Straight-nosed Pipe-fish.
6. Worm Pipe-fish. 7. Sea Horse (p. 70)

Twaite Shad (p. 62)
Smelt (p. 64)

Pl. 16

Pl. 17   Salmon, male (*above*) and female (p. 63)

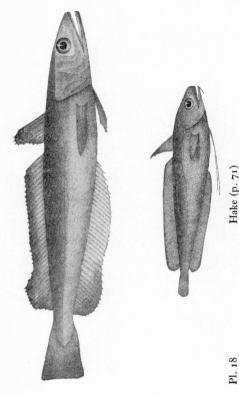

Hake (p. 71)
Greater Fork-beard (p. 79)

Pl. 18

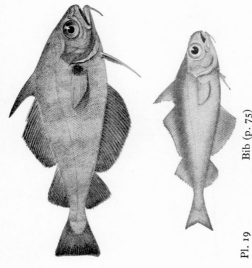

Bib (p. 75)
Poor Cod (p. 76)

Pl. 19

Sea Trout, male (*above*) and female (p. 64)

Pl. 20

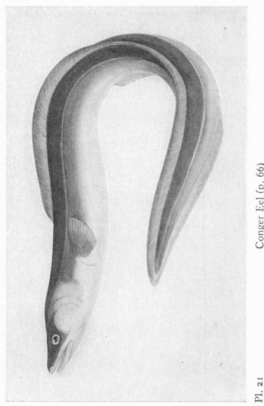

Conger Eel (p. 66)

Pl. 21

Coal-fish (p. 77)
Four-bearded Rockling (p. 82)

Pl. 22

Three-bearded Rockling (p. 81)
Five-bearded Rockling (p. 81)

Pl. 23

Cod (p. 73)
Haddock (p. 74)

Pl. 24

Opah (p. 83)

Pl. 25

Whiting (p. 76)
Pollack (p. 78)

Pl. 26

Pl. 27   John Dory (p. 83)
                           Boar fish (p. 85)

Common Ling (p. 79)
Blue Ling

Pl. 28

Horse Mackerel (p. 88)
Armed Bullhead (p. 131)

Pl. 29

Bass (p. 86)
Common Sea Bream (p. 94)

Pl. 30

Pl. 31

1. Greater Sand Eel (p. 99)
2. Lesser Sand Eel (p. 99)
3. Lesser Weever (p. 101)

Red Mullet (p. 92)
Greater Weever (p. 103)

Pl. 32

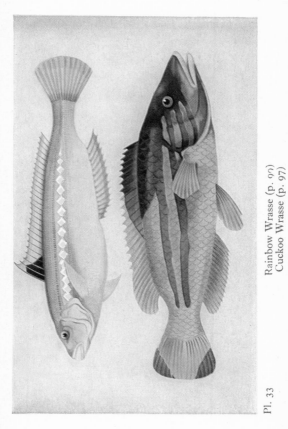

Rainbow Wrasse (p. 92)
Cuckoo Wrasse (p. 97)

Pl. 33

Short-finned Tunny (p. 106)

Pl. 34

Pl. 35   1. Shanny (p. 117).   2. Yarrell's
Blenny (p. 118)   3. Montagu's Blenny (p. 118)

Corkwing (p. 98)
Ballan Wrasse (p. 97)

Pl. 36

Pl. 37   Rock Goby, female (p. 111)
Rock Goby, male
Fries' Goby (p. 111)

Butterfly Blenny (p. 118)
Viviparous Blenny (p. 120)

Pl. 38

Sand Smelt (p. 125)
Boyer's Sand Smelt

Pl. 39

Pl. 40   Painted Goby (p. 112)
Diminutive Goby, female
Diminutive Goby, male (p. 113)

Spotted Dragonet (p. 116)
Fifteen-spined Stickleback (p. 134)

Pl. 41

Yellow Gurnard (p. 128)
Red Gurnard (p. 129)

Pl. 42

Pl. 43 1. Cornish Sucker. 2. Connemara Sucker.
3. Two-spotted Sucker (p. 150)

Cat-fish (p. 121)
Black Goby (p. 111)

Pl. 44

Butterfish (p. 119)
Norway Haddock (p. 126)

Pl. 45

Pl. 46   Bloch's Topknot (p. 139)
Scald-fish (p. 138)

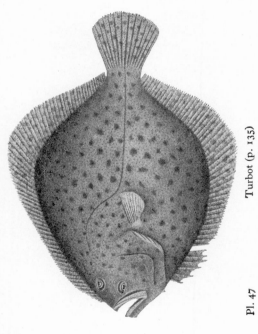

Turbot (p. 135)

Pl. 47

Grey Mullet (p. 123)
Four-horned Sea Scorpion (p. 131)

Pl. 48

Pl. 49

Streaked Gurnard
Grey Gurnard (p. 127)

Megrim (p. 137)

Pl. 50

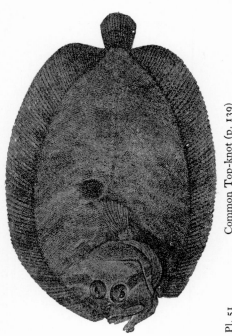

Common Top-knot (p. 139)

Pl. 51

Pl. 52   Long-spined Sea Scorpion, male (*above*) and female (p. 130)

Pl. 53 Lump-sucker, male (*above*) and female (p. 132)

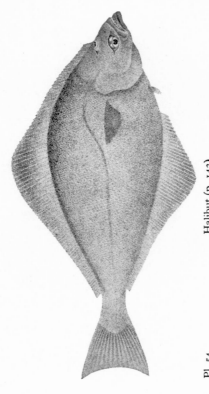

Halibut (p. 143)

Pl. 54

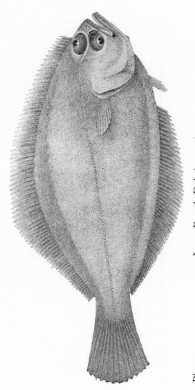

Long Rough Dab (p. 144)

Pl. 55

Pl. 56   Brill (p. 136)
Plaice (p. 140)

Common Sole (p. 145)
French or Sand Sole (p. 147)

Pl. 57

Dab (p. 141)

Pl. 58

Lemon Sole (p. 143)

Pl. 59

Pl. 60

Solenette (p. 147)
Thickback or Variegated Sole (p. 147)

Pl. 61   Common Sun-fish (p. 148)

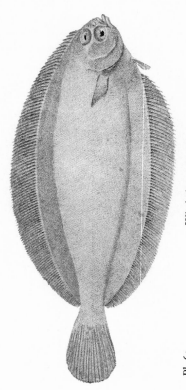

Witch (p. 142)

Pl. 62

Flounder (p. 141)

Pl. 63

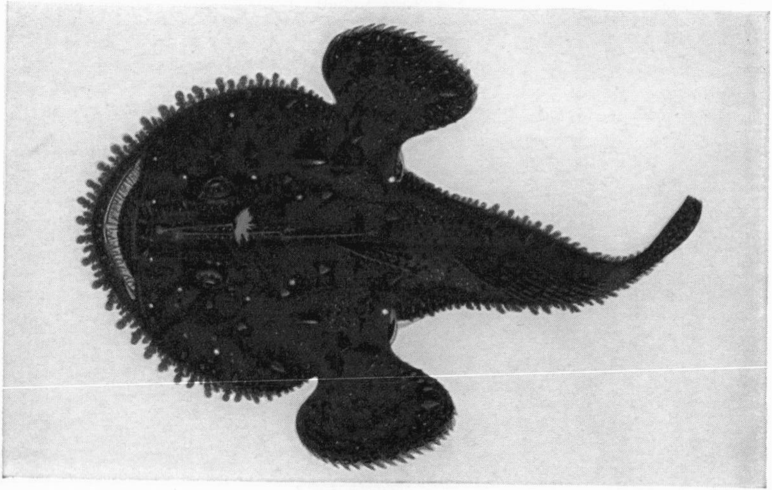

Angler Fish (p. 151)

Pl. 64

Gurnard, the deep-blue colour of the large pectoral fins being largely responsible for at least two of its names. It is the largest of our common gurnards, attaining a length of two feet in favourable conditions, with a weight of up to eleven pounds. The south-west coast of England is its most general haunt but it is more common in the North Sea than is generally realized. The breeding time extends from the early part of the summer to October.

There are spines along the base of the dorsal fins.

The Red Gurnard, *Trigla cuculus* (Plate 42), otherwise the Elleck, Soldier, Rochet or Red Fish, is the smallest of our three more common Gurnards. It is found all the year round off the south and south-west coasts of England, the coasts of Ireland and, doubtless, the North Sea as well, for it is common in winter and summer in the Thames estuary. The scales on the lateral line are in the form of narrow plates without spines but there is a ridge of spines along the base of the dorsal fins. The colour is a deep red. The length is up to one foot. The spawning period is from April to June.

Of the three less common species, the least rare would appear to be the Piper, *Trigla lyra*, and this must surely not be considered a very uncommon fish of the south-west coast. Should you encounter it you will find that the bones of the head project from the front of the upper jaw as two toothed plates. By this it can easily be recognized. The pectoral fins are as large as those of the Tub-fish but they are not brightly coloured.

The two other species are too rare to require mention.

The Bullheads, as the members of this family are sometimes called, are closely related to the Gurnards which they very much resemble. In freshwater the Miller's Thumb is a familiar representative whilst the three species of marine habit all keep close inshore. None are of any economic value whatsoever and even the angler from the seaside pier after a long fruitless day would as soon land a crab or starfish as a Bullhead. Indeed, Pennant, one of the earliest and most graphic of British students of fish, remarks: 'The colour of this fish is as disagreeable as its form, being dusky, mixed with a dusky yellow; the belly whitish.' I rather feel that he summed the whole thing up very nicely.

He was, of course, referring to the Father Lasher, *Cottus scorpius*, otherwise known as the Sea Scorpion, Short-spined Cottus, Bull-trout or Sea Toad. It is a winter spawner—December to March—and the eggs are adhesive and demersal, sticking to the rocks and weeds of the shallows. The length may be up to twelve inches or more, but I have yet to see a specimen from the south-east coast of more than ten inches in length.

Our three species may be distinguished as follows: in *C. scorpius* the first dorsal fin is nearly as high as the second. There is a spine above the eye and four principal spines on the gill-cover, the uppermost of which is short and smooth.

The Long-spined Sea Scorpion, *C. bubalis* (Plate 52), is an equally common though smaller species. On some parts of the coast it is less dingy coloured than elsewhere, taking on a distinct red colour. It may be readily distinguished by the five principal spines on the gill cover, the uppermost of which is long and rough.

The Four-horned Cottus, *Cottus quadricornis* (Plate 48), frequents the deeper water and is of a more northerly habitat. By the two pairs of large rough tubercles on the top of the head and the one or two rows of tubercles along its sides, it may be easily separated from the two foregoing species.

THE ARMED BULLHEAD   *AGONIDAE*

The Armed Bullhead (Plate 29) or Pogge, *Agonus cataphractus*, is a fish that looks perpetually sorry for itself. If anything, it is uglier than the Bullheads and economically as useless. A typically northern fish it is found all round the coasts of the British Isles where it is very common indeed. In the summer it comes close inshore and retreats to the deeper water in the winter. The eggs are laid in early autumn, presumably just before the winter migration takes place, and are designed to withstand rough usage, the capsules being remarkably tough. It is as well they are tough for, although having the advantage of being demersal, they yet have to spend practically the entire winter being pushed around on the seabed. Hatching takes place any time between January and April but no one seems to know exactly what will precipitate hatching or delay it. For three months or so the fry will swim near the surface but at about three-quarters of an inch in length the little Pogges will sink to the bottom where they will remain for pretty well the remainder of their days.

This is a northern family with only very few species to its name. The only really common one is the Lump Fish or Lump-sucker, *Cyclopterus lumpus* (Plate 53), otherwise the Sea Hen, Cock Paddle, Sea Owl, Stone Clagger, and I do not know how many other local names. A lumpy sort of fish, as the plate well shows, it is chiefly known to fame for the solicitude of the parents for their eggs.

The adults of the two sexes are of a rocky colour on the upper surface; the female is a yellowish-white on the undersurface and the male, at breeding time, of a bright brick-red colour. The eggs are deposited some time during the spring, early or late according to the individual, in shallow water. As there may be over a hundred thousand eggs in the demersal mass the male has to provide a stream of water to keep those on the inside from dying from lack of oxygen. To achieve this the fond parent anchors itself by means of a suctorial disc situated between the junction of the pelvic fins on the underside and with the rays of those same fins continually fans the water over the eggs.

The male, which is the smaller, is generally credited with being the guardian of the eggs but the female, if necessary, will also take on the task. This I know from an incident at Southend Aquarium in 1956 when a nine-pound lump-sucker was brought in by a shrimp trawler and housed in a separate tank. After a few days she laid a large cluster of pale pink eggs and for a week mounted guard over them until they went bad from not having been fertilized. A few weeks later she also died.

The hazards with which the faithful parent is

faced are considerable. In the course of the vigil the tide may retreat so far that its back is exposed to the air and then the birds have an easy prey.

The young at first seek the upper layers of the water and later swim at the same level as the whitebait. In the Thames estuary specimens of an inch and a half in length are found in the catch during February. In April, with a length of two and a half inches and a weight of a quarter of an ounce, they are caught in the shrimp trawl. At this size they begin to exhibit the rows of tubercles along the sides which are a feature of the adult, and are bright green in colour.

The food of the adult consists largely of whitebait or other small fishes. These are generally plentiful in winter, so that is when this fish does its feeding. In the spring it is too busy looking after its eggs to eat and in the summer the type of food it prefers is scarce.

The flesh is flabby and is only eaten when nothing else is available. In any case, it is only the male that is eaten, its flesh being slightly firmer. In Denmark, where it is known as the Sea-hare, its eggs are collected and treated in the appropriate manner and sold as Danish caviare.

One reason for the general flabbiness is the fact that its stomach is nearly always distended with water. Consequently, the stomach fluids are so diluted that they cannot cope with the fungoid growths and large bacilli which are found there.

THE SEA SNAILS *LIPARIDAE*

These little fishes are most aptly named for they do indeed, resemble both in shape and colouration the common garden slug. There are two species in our fauna and both have a preference for our northern coasts. They are a plump, soft, greasy-skinned fish, brownish or purplish in colour and have a preference for the deeper water in winter and come inshore for the summer.

The Common Sea Snail, *Liparis liparis*, spawns in January, the eggs adhering in masses to seaweeds and zoophytes (the sea moss or whiteweed sold for table decoration) either in shallow water or up to a depth of thirty fathoms. The fry spend their youth in the plankton, later sinking to the bottom. The length of the adult may be five inches or slightly more.

Montagu's Sea Snail, *L. montagui*, is slightly smaller than the common sea snail, otherwise it is much the same. The spawning season is from January to March, the eggs being laid in masses attached to weeds. It is more common off the Scottish coast than in the south, although I have found it in east-coast estuaries.

THE STICKLEBACKS
GASTEROSTEIDAE

There are three species of sticklebacks (Plate 41) found in the British Isles, two of which—the Three-spined Stickleback, *Gasterosteus aculeatus*, and the Ten-spined Stickleback, *Pygosteus pungitius*, sometimes enter brackish water when heavy rains cause the rivers to rise and so carry them down to the sea. The Fifteen-spined Stickleback, *Spinachia spinachia*, is a marine species and is found all round our coasts in shallow water, whether rocky or otherwise.

As with the two other species the male builds a nest in the weeds at breeding time into which it entices the female. The male also undergoes a colour change at this time but not, as with the freshwater species, to red on the underside, but to blue. The female retains the normal colour, olive-green.

It is an unusual fish and when a large specimen of, say eight inches, is caught its identity puzzles many people.

THE FLATFISHES

The flatfishes swim on their sides and not on their stomachs as do the rays and the skates. Both eyes are situated on the upper side which carries a protective colouring. The underside is whitish although it is not rare to find a specimen with patches of colour there also.

Apart from the herring, salmon and cod kind, no other group of fishes has received so much attention from professional ichthyologists. No other kind is economically more important, at least five different species being commonly found on the average fishmonger's slab at all seasons.

They fall roughly into four groups, according to the side on which the eyes are situated and whether there are teeth all round the jaw or only on the underside.

Bothidae

The members of this family have the eyes on the left side, the mouth is large, at the end of the snout, and the teeth and jaws are equal on both sides.

The Turbot, *Scophthalmus maximus* (Plate 47), has a large, diamond-shaped body with no scales but with blunt bony tubercles. This is one of the choicest fishes of the sea for the table and always commands high prices.

The south and west coasts are the favourite habitat and spawning takes place there from April to June, the female laying up to ten million eggs—surely one of the most prolific of fishes. Frank Buckland refers to a turbot weighing twenty-three pounds that had a roe weighing five pounds nine ounces and contained no less than fourteen million, three hundred and eleven thousand eggs. He also mentions having made a plaster cast of a specimen which weighed thirty-two pounds. In the ordinary way the male will have a length of seventeen inches and the female up to twenty-eight inches.

The eggs are planktonic, then they sink but not, I should think, quite to the bottom, for the larvae are found frequently in the surface tow-net. When they are nearly a quarter of an inch in length the larvae change from their original state of having an eye on each side of the head to the eyes being on the same side, as in the adult.

In the Brill, *Scophthalmus rhombus* (Plate 56), the body is more oval and is covered with smooth scales. Like the turbot it is a voracious feeder and will greedily devour the young of other flatfishes. Also, neither species is particularly interested in its prey if it is dead. Consequently, the angler should use his bait as fresh as possible. Sand eels are a great favourite with the brill.

The habitat, too, is similar. Sandbanks are a great attraction, yet for some reason or other the Goodwin Sands off Kent are by no means good turbot or brill grounds. In the ordinary way, although they prefer depths of less than forty fathoms, they are not usually found in estuaries, yet I frequently find them in the shrimp trawl in the Thames, even as far from the sea as Canvey Point.

The females preponderate over the males in the proportion of three to two. Spawning takes place off the east coast of Scotland from April to June and this has also been observed to be the case at Grimsby, Plymouth and off the west of Ireland. The early development immediately after leaving the egg is not known with any certainty, but it probably follows that of the turbot very closely. When the fish is about half an inch in length one eye gradually moves round the head from what will now be the under side and joins the one on the top. At a length of three-quarters of an inch the transition is completed, but the young brill may not descend to the seabed until it is an inch in length. The female lays a number of pale inky coloured eggs, up to eight hundred thousand in number.

It grows to a length of eighteen inches although there is a record of a specimen with a length of two feet.

In the Megrim, *Lepidorhombus whiff-iagonis* (Plate 50), the body is narrow and thin with rough scales. The eyes and mouth are very large. The colour is light yellow.

This fish has given rise to more misunderstandings than most other fishes because it is known by so many different names, even in the same locality. I cannot say that its scientific name is a very helpful one either. In Cornwall it is principally known as the Whiff or Lantern-fish. Elsewhere it is called Mary Sole, Carter, Sail-fluke, Queen Sole, whilst in Dublin it is known as the White Sole or Ox Sole. Hawkers make a point of calling it a Lemon Sole and I have, in a seaside restaurant, had some served to me as Dover soles, a very poor substitute, for the flesh is dry and most uninteresting.

It is abundant off the south-west coast of England and off the west coasts of Scotland and Ireland and as far north as the Shetlands, yet it is fairly rare in the North Sea and the Irish Sea. There is a wide depth range of from four to two hundred fathoms. Spawning takes place from March to April, the female laying nearly half a million eggs. The subsequent development is along similar lines to that of the turbot. The largest recorded specimen had a length of twenty-three and a half inches.

Next there is the Scald-fish, *Arnoglossus laterna* (Plate 46), which has smaller eyes and mouth than the megrim. Although the scales are large the skin is very thin and easily tears off. The first rays of the dorsal fin of the male are very much elongated but this is not so in the female.

It is a fairly common little fish (maximum length about eight inches) around the British Isles save on the eastern side of Britain where it is very rarely caught. There is only one record from the Thames estuary; a five-inch specimen was taken in a shrimp trawl off Leigh on 21 April 1900.

Breeding time is April to May, probably extending into June. Until recent years the larvae had not been found; the development is similar to that of the turbot.

It is readily recognizable on the fishmonger's slab as the flesh is nearly bare, just as though it had been scalded.

The Top-knots, three species of which inhabit British waters, may be distinguished from the rest of the flatfishes by their short faces, very long dorsal and ventral fins and the lack of a free root to the tail. The dorsal fin commences very far forward, in front of the eyes in fact, and the two fins are continued on to the underside beneath the root of the tail. The mouth is large and the scales are very spiny, the spines projecting upwards and so giving the fish a hairy appearance.

The roughest of the three is the Common Top-knot, *Zeugopterus punctatus* (Plate 51), the largest and most widely distributed of the three species. In Cornwall it is called the Browny or Bastard Brill. It has the remarkable habit of adhering to rocks and for this reason, perhaps, is not so frequently captured as it might otherwise be. The length may be up to eight inches.

The One-spotted or Bloch's Top-knot, *Phrynorhombus regius* (Plate 46), has the first dorsal fin-ray elongated and there is a single round spot on the upper side towards the tail. The underside is very rough. It is a more southern species and is found in sandy bays on the west coasts of England and Ireland and in the English Channel.

The Norwegian Top-knot, *Phrynorhombus norvegicus*, is found on the west coast of Ireland, and is the smallest, having a length of about four inches. The throat fins are separated from the ventral fin; in the other two they are united. None of the three has any commercial value.

Pleuronectidae

This family can be divided into two groups. In the first of these the eyes are on the right side, the mouth is at the end of the snout and the teeth are most developed on the underside.

The most valuable member of this family,

without a doubt, is the familiar plaice, *Pleuronectes platessa* (Plate 56), which is found abundantly all round the British coast. Being of a sedentary habit there has always been the danger of its being over-fished, especially as it is such a favourite in most households. There has been considerable research by the various fishery boards and in consequence our knowledge of its life story is a fairly complete one.

In its very young days its food will be the molluscs and crustacea, both larval and adult, of the plankton; then, when it sinks to the bottom, it seeks out the small worms and crustacea which have their being there. In the adult state larger molluscs, mostly bivalves such as the cockle, are eaten, shell and all. On the Dogger Bank, a famous plaice ground, the principal food is a member of the Donax family of Wedge-shells.

In the English Channel and the North Sea spawning takes place early in the year, from January to March, in the latter area possibly extending into early May. On the west of Ireland and Scotland the season is somewhat later. The extrusion of the eggs takes some time, up to a fortnight, starting very slowly at first and speeding up towards the end. The eggs are very large for a floating kind being a twelfth of an inch in diameter. When hatched out the larvae make their way slowly to the bottom, changing on the way to the adult shape. At first, as in all flatfishes, they have the appearance of an ordinary round fish with an eye on each side of the head. Gradually the eye on the underside moves round to the top-side, as I have described with the turbot. Two methods are adopted to achieve this end. The most common one is for it to move round the head.

In species such as the sole and turbot in which the dorsal fin extends to beyond the eyes in the adult, the fry will have this fin falling short of the eyes. In some species the eye will move through the head.

At three years old the plaice may have a length of seventeen inches, this depending largely on the food available. Its principal characteristics are its small scales embedded in the skin, the bony knobs on the head behind the eyes and the red spots on the upper side.

The Flounder, *Platichthys flesus* (Plate 63), has rough tubercles along the bases of the marginal fins and along the lateral line. It is essentially a fish of the estuaries, and there is not an estuary in the British Isles where it is not to be found. If there are no barriers it will even ascend into fresh water but it has not been found in fresh water cut off from the sea unless some one put it there. In the matter of food the fluke, as it is sometimes called, is not fussy: it will eat worms, molluscs, shrimps and in fresh water, even aquatic insects.

Reversed flounders are not uncommon, that is, with the eyes on the right side. There is a fallacy about this to which some of the older fishermen adhere strongly. It is that the left-sided ones are males and that the right-sided ones are females. Two other fallacies also persist. They are that the various coloured masses of eggs found on the foreshore are the eggs of the flounder, whereas they are the eggs of marine worms. The other is that the seed-like projections, due to disease, which are found on its back are also its eggs. The truth is they spawn in the open sea from February to June, with March and April as the maximum months. The eggs are planktonic.

The Dab, *Limanda limanda* (Plate 58), has scales

with toothed edges and so the skin has a rough feel. Its most characteristic feature, however, is the rounded curve of the lateral line above the pectoral fin. The colour is light brown and it is sometimes covered on the back with small spots (they are not red like those of the plaice) which gradually vanish when the fish is taken from the water.

Although abundant in the outer parts of estuaries and often far up them, the dab also ventures into depths of fifty fathoms. In some places small crustacea, small hermit and other crabs are the favourite food whilst in others molluscs will be favoured. In St. Andrews Bay worms and sand-stars form the main diet.

The eggs are the smallest of any of the flatfishes, with the exception of *Arnoglossus*, having a diameter of only 0.8 mm., and they are deposited in March, April and May. Their development is along similar lines to that of the other flatfishes. The maximum length of the female may be seventeen inches, with that of the male an inch less.

The Witch, otherwise known as the Long Flounder, Pole Dab, Witch Sole, *Glyptocephalus cynoglossus* (Plate 62), is found around most parts of the British coast but is rare in the English Channel. It is not a fish of the shallows, it prefers depths of from seventy to seven hundred fathoms. The average length of the female is seventeen inches and that of the male is fifteen inches.

Superficially, there is a strong resemblance in this species to the common sole, and cunning restaurateurs and fishmongers often try to palm them off for the more expensive and better tasting article. A close examination is not necessary in order to separate them. The tail of the witch is longer and the pectoral fin is larger than in the sole. The body is thin and flat and the colour of the upper surface is pale brown, whilst the underside has a smoky appearance. Also there are more rays in the dorsal and ventral fins than in the sole, viz. 102 to 115 in the dorsal and 86 to 97 in the ventral, whereas in the sole there are 73 to 90 rays in the dorsal and 61 to 74 in the ventral. But if you do not have the time to count the fin rays you will find the mouth the readiest means of distinguishing them. In the sole the snout projects beyond the mouth but in the witch the mouth projects beyond the snout.

In the Lemon Dab, otherwise Lemon Sole, Slippery Dab or Smear Dab, *Microstomus kitt* (Plate 59), the scales are small and smooth and the skin is very slimy. There is a slight curve in the lateral line above the pectoral fin but it is not so pronounced as in the common dab. The colour is brownish yellow marbled with round or oval spots, some light and some dark. The shape is oval. Here again is a fish with a preference for deeper water and it is found all round the British Isles at some distance from the shore in depths of from twenty to forty fathoms, although it has been found in the outer part of the Thames estuary in the Wallet. Breeding time is protracted and extends from April to September. The eggs only just float; if they were laid in brackish water they would sink.

There are two British species in this family in which the mouth is large and the jaws are similar on both sides. The other members of the Pleuronectidae have the underside of the jaws most developed.

In this group the lordly Halibut appears, *Hippoglossus hippoglossus* (Plate 54), the largest of all the world's flatfishes. There are authenticated British records of specimens seven and a half feet in length with a weight of 320 pounds. In October 1957 a halibut was landed at Grimsby which weighed no less than 504 pounds and was estimated as being over sixty years old. It was one of the largest, if not the largest, true fish to be landed in Britain. The majority captured range from two to six feet in length.

The skin is smooth and of a dark olive colour with some marbling. The lateral line is curved above the pectoral fin.

Iceland, the Faroes and our northern shores in depths of fifty to one hundred and twenty fathoms are the source of the greater part of our supply, and the major part of that is obtained by long-lining rather than by trawling. Off the Faroes the chief halibut baits are herrings and young coal-fish but they have been known to pick up a haddock already caught on the line and swallow it and the hook as well. Generally speaking any small fish will do for bait and in some areas plaice are favoured. The favourite haunt seems to be rocky ground where trawling is difficult and this would explain the preponderance of line-caught halibut.

So far as we know the eggs, about an eighth of an inch in diameter, are of the floating kind and are laid between April and August with an extension either way according to the locality.

The Long Rough Dab, *Hippoglossoides platessoides* (Plate 55), closely resembles its near relative the halibut, apart, of course, from the great disparity in size. It also differs in having a rough skin due to spines on the hinder edge of the scales, a straight lateral line and proportionately larger eyes and mouth.

The habitat and range are much the same as that of the halibut. As regards food, one may refer to the Tenth Report of the Scottish Fishery Board in which reference is made to the contents of the stomachs of 569 long rough dabs taken from the Firth of Forth. The different kinds of marine animals, in the order of their abundance, were as follows: crustacea (49%), echinoderms, fish, marine worms and molluscs.

The spawning and subsequent development of the larvae follow closely on that of the other flat-fishes except that the fry, when they sink to the bottom, choose deeper water than is the case with any other species. The length is up to sixteen inches.

THE TRUE SOLES *SOLEIDAE*

In the members of this family the eyes are on the right side and the snout projects beyond the jaws and the front margin of the head is curved. The jaws are larger on the underside and there is also a 'beard' there composed of short projections from the skin. The shape of the body is a narrow oval.

The Common Sole, *Solea solea* (Plate 57), like the other members of its family is more a southern than a northern species. Although the plaice constitutes the larger fishery the sole is held in higher regard for the table and several hundred different ways of cooking it have been evolved from the familiar 'Sole bonne femme' to the majestic 'Sole Royale' in which it is served surrounded by shredded lobster meat and smothered with shrimp sauce.

The members of this family are very similar in appearance, but *S. solea* may be distinguished by its larger pectoral fins, that on the upper surface having a black spot at its outer end, and the nostrils on the two sides being similar.

The principal British grounds are off the coast of Ireland, the Irish Sea, the English and Bristol Channels and the North Sea, principally on shoals in between five to twenty fathoms of water.

The favourite diet seems to be of marine worms such as the small kind dwelling in the sand or in sandy tubes. Brittle stars, small crustaceans and molluscs also are eaten when, presumably, other types of food are not available. The food is sought out by smell and it has been observed in the aquarium that the sole also seeks its food by gliding over the sand, tapping it gently with its head, thereby thrusting the projections on the underside of the head into the sand and so using them as feelers. Like several other flatfishes, particularly the plaice, it has the habit of burying itself partially and lying in wait for its unsuspecting prey.

Spawning takes place from March to June in the open sea, the eggs being buoyant and containing a great number of minute oil globules. The larvae possess an air-bladder so one might well assume that until they are fairly well developed they occupy the upper layers of the water. The fry use the estuaries as nurseries, for at all seasons the shrimpers find 'lamb's tongues,' as they call the little flatfishes generally, in the catch. In the estuaries they will find ideal food for their growth and in their first year they may be six or more inches in length. They are probably mature at about ten inches in length and eventually attain a length of eighteen inches or even more.

The Sand Sole or French Sole, *Pegusa lascaris* (Plate 57), must be considered as being a rather rare British fish and although stragglers may travel some distance to the north it is essentially a southern fish. It is referred to here because it is frequently to be seen at the fishmongers for it is landed by trawlermen operating at the entrance to the English Channel.

It is very similar in appearance to the common sole but it may be distinguished by the front nostril on the blind side being much enlarged and fringed on the outer edge. The scales are larger and the colour a brighter yellow with numerous small black spots and golden flecks. The dorsal fin commences farther forward, at the extremity of the snout, in fact. The length is between eight and ten inches. Very little is known about its spawning habits and not a lot about either its eggs or larvae.

The Thickback Sole, *Microchirus variegatus* (Plate 60), is fairly common off the coasts of Devon and Cornwall in deep water but is rare elsewhere.

The pectoral fins are very small, rudimentary almost, and the mouth is straighter than in the other soles and is nearer the snout. The ventral and dorsal fins do not reach the root of the tail. The colour is distinctive, being brownish-red with five shadowy black bands across the body. The length does not usually exceed nine inches.

Spawning takes place in April and, although eggs and the very young larvae have been taken, little is known of its early development.

The Solenette, *Microchirus boscanion* (Plate 60), is quite common all round our coasts and, as it does not grow to more than five inches in length, is frequently mistaken for the young of the common sole, from which it can readily be separated. It occupies the same shallow grounds as the young sole and has the same taste in food.

It can be recognized by its pectoral fins, which are so rudimentary as to be almost invisible. The dorsal fin extends to the snout and both this fin and the ventral fin extend as far as the tail. The colour is similar to that of the sole, with the same kind of dark spots, but at intervals along the dorsal and ventral fins are distinct black lines, each corresponding to a fin ray.

Spawning is from April to August, the eggs being of the floating kind as also are the larvae. At quite a small size—less than half an inch—the development into the adult form is completed and then the fish sinks to the bottom.

THE SUN-FISHES   *MOLIDAE*

Every summer, from somewhere or other around our coast, come reports of the capture of one or other of the oddly shaped Sun-fishes (Plate 61). Off the west coast of Ireland, at that time of the year, they are a regular feature of the seascape as they bask on the surface.

Of the two species which visit us only one does so frequently. This is the Short Sun-fish, *Mola mola*, which, at seven or eight feet in length, may weigh a hundredweight for each foot of its length. Because of its foreshortened appearance it is sometimes called the Head-fish. Even more remarkable than the shape is its spinal cord which does not extend for the whole length of the body as in other fishes but has a length of about an inch.

Then there is its skin which is not only as tough as shagreen but is also reinforced underneath by a layer of cartilaginous material three inches thick.

The flesh looks like fat bacon and when it is cooked it is more like jelly and is a complete loss so far as the housewife is concerned. The liver is said to be rich in oil and at one time the fish was hunted with harpoons off Ireland. This would be made possible by its habit of dozing on the surface with its dorsal fin sticking out of the water. When harpooned, however, it moves quickly enough, its curious shape making rapid and deep diving possible. Murie records a specimen five feet two inches in length and four feet three inches in depth and weighing 196 pounds being caught by shrimpers off Southend in 1872, and another, weighing half a hundredweight, being observed by shrimpers off Canvey Island in September 1897 whilst they were returning to Leigh. They rowed up to it and grasped the projecting fin and whisked the fish into the boat. He referred to the fact that it did not possess true teeth but had a turtle-like mouth, with hard gum-plates.

The Oblong or Truncated Sun-fish, *Ranzania truncata*, is a much smaller and much rarer visitor. It is of similar compressed shape but instead of its colour being a dull, brownish hue, as is that of *M. mola*, it is a beautiful violet with a pale underside. The scales are like plates and are closely set. Both this species and the foregoing doubtless journey north with the Gulf Stream and this would account for their being more frequently found off the west of Ireland and south-west of England.

In these little shore-loving fishes there is a suctorial disc situated under the throat and formed partly by the base of the pectoral fins and modified bones of the pelvic girdle. It is large, quoit-like in shape and leathery. By this means the fish can adhere firmly to rocks and stones even when the waves are boisterous. This habit has earned for it the name of Cling-fish.

Like some of the other inhabitants of the rock pools and shallows it lays its eggs in an empty shell or in a crevice in the rocks for protection. Sometimes they will be attached to a clump of zoophytes and the mass may have a diameter of three-eighths of an inch. The eggs are elongated and are deposited in June or July.

There are four species found on the coasts of the British Isles, each with its own distinguishing features. The largest is the Cornish Sucker, *Lepadogaster gouani* (Plate 43). Gouan, after whom it is named, called it 'The Barber' from the fancied resemblance to a barber's shaving basin of his day. The length is about four inches and it is remarkable for the two eye spots on the top of the head. The dorsal fin is continuous with the caudal fin and consists of more than ten rays.

In the Connemara Sucker, *Lepadogaster candollii* (Plate 43), the dorsal fin also has more than ten rays, but it is distinct from the caudal fin.

The Two-spotted Sucker, *Lepadogaster bimaculatus* (Plate 43), has less than eight rays in the dorsal fin, and the caudal has twelve rays. It is also the smallest species, with a length of only two inches. There is a dark spot on each side at the posterior edge of the pectoral fins.

The Small-headed Sucker, *Lepadogaster micro-cephalus*, although by some considered to be only a variety of the aforementioned can be distinguished by the seventeen to nineteen rays of the caudal fin.

THE ANGLER FISHES   *LOPHIIDAE*

There can hardly be a spot around our coasts on which, at one time or another, an angler fish has not been stranded. It is an occurrence that never fails to cause considerable speculation as to the identity of the creature. The grotesque shape and the huge mouth bristling with teeth and the unusual shape of the dorsal fin certainly set it aside from other fishes.

The habit of the Angler Fish, *Lophius piscatorius* (Plate 64), otherwise Pocket-fish, Monk fish, Fiddler and Fishing-frog, is to half bury itself in the seabed and wait for a victim to be attracted by its lure. This consists of a flap of shiny skin attached to the free end of the long first dorsal ray. This is separate and can be inclined forward over the mouth. Dr. D. P. Wilson at the Plymouth Marine Laboratory has had considerable experience in observing the feeding habits of this fish in captivity. He records how the lure is agitated with the obvious intent of attracting its victims, sometimes even dangling over the gaping maw below. But he makes no reference to the old theory that if a fish grasps the lure it is suddenly whipped downwards into the waiting mouth. This is an assumption that has survived for centuries but which has no apparent foundation on actual fact.

At one time this fish was held of little account as food and in any case its repulsive appearance would repel any possible purchasers. Gradually, fishermen used the tail end to supplement their food supply and found it to be quite good. Nowadays it is beheaded and skinned and sold with the Cat-fish and Monk or Angel-fish as rock salmon.

There are several instances of its eggs being laid in British waters. One such incident is of more than passing interest. One June in the 'nineties of the last century Mr. Matthias Dunn of Mevagissy, a great observer of fish, noticed from the cliffs a large, dark patch on the water below. The next day he took a boat, found the object and brought it ashore. It was between twenty and thirty feet long and eighteen inches wide. It was a mass of eggs far advanced in development and the young fish being black could be seen in it 'like currants in a cake,' to use Mr. Dunn's words, and struggling to get out. A large number were taken to the Plymouth aquarium where they hatched out.

The length of these fishes may exceed six feet. A specimen which I examined in 1932 had been found stranded on Shoebury beach. It had choked itself trying to swallow a three-pound skate. The length was five feet and the weight forty-eight pounds.

INDEX

INDEX

PRINTED FOR THE PUBLISHERS BY WM. CLOWES AND SONS, LTD.,
LONDON AND BECCLES
1883.363